12842 MCFED

BELFAST INSTITUTE

3 7777 00028 1519

DATE DUE AT THE LIBRARY LAST NAMED BELOW
Application for renewal, quoting date due and all details in the panel
above, may be made in person, writing or by telephone

Millfield Library
College of Technology
BELFAST

10 OCT 1991

16 APR 1996

16·12·96

2 1 NOV 2005

17 JAN 2007

WITHDRAWN

-- JUL 2012

S. 20

THE BUILDING ENVELOPE

Applications of new technology cladding

Alan J. Brookes

Chris Grech

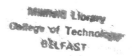

Muirhead Library
College of Technology
BELFAST

Butterworth Architecture

London Boston Singapore Sydney Toronto Wellington

Butterworth Architecture
is an imprint of Butterworth Scientific

 PART OF REED INTERNATIONAL P.L.C.

All rights reserved. No part of this publication may be reproduced in any
material form (including photocopying or storing it in any medium by
electronic means and whether or not transiently or incidentally to some
other use of this publication) without the written permission of the
copyright owner except in accordance with the provisions of the
Copyright, Designs and Patents Act 1988 or under the terms of a licence
issued by the Copyright Licensing Agency Ltd, 33–34 Alfred Place,
London, England WC1E 7DP. Applications for the copyright owner's
written permission to reproduce any part of this publication should be
addressed to the Publishers.

Warning: The doing of an unauthorized act in relation to a copyright work
may result in both a civil claim for damages and criminal prosecution.

This book is sold subject to the Standard Conditions of Sale of Net Books
and may not be re-sold in the UK below the net price given by the
Publishers in their current price list.

First published 1990

© Butterworth & Co. (Publishers) Ltd, 1990

British Library Cataloguing in Publication Data
The Building envelope.
   1. Building components: Cladding
   I. Brookes, Alan, *1939–*   II. Grech, Chris
   693

ISBN 0–408–50030–1

Library of Congress-in-Publication
Data applied for

Photoset by Activity Ltd, Salisbury, Wiltshire
Printed and bound in Great Britain by Courier International Ltd,
Tiptree, Essex

Preface

In making the selection of these 33 case studies of buildings which incorporate newer forms of construction technology we are mindful of those times when students of architecture have sought similar information as a basis for their own work. This selection, therefore, to some extent has been influenced by their requests for more information on these particular projects, which vary from a small house in Australia to the construction at Stansted Airport. What is certain, within present architectural literature, is the scarcity of constructional information related to recent buildings of architectural merit.

Architectural criticism of buildings often deals only briefly with their technical aspects – one possible explanation for this is that the critics themselves may lack the necessary information required to make a technical appraisal. The exception to this would be the excellent technical studies prepared for the *Architects' Journal* by John Winter and others, and many of the photographs and illustrations included in this book have been drawn from that source.

Many well-known architects also prefer to explain their work within a broad cultural context rather than deal with the specific issues of construction. It is, for example, quite difficult to obtain information on the stone facade to Stirling's Staatsgalerie or its curtain walling system, although innumerable books exist dealing with the overall design and philosophy of the building. This has not always been the case: Joseph Paxton was doing nothing unusual in presenting his designs for the Crystal Palace in the 1850s to the meeting of the Institute of Civil Engineers for their criticism of its construction and (paradoxically, in view of its later history) comments on its fire resistance. Some practices continue with this tradition – (for example, the regular meetings by Arup Associates to present the work of the different design teams to each other). Generally speaking, however, there is not a proper dialogue between the members of the architectural profession on the merits or disadvantages of the various constructional solutions.

Larger practices employ their own specialist groups dealing with performance requirements and specifica-

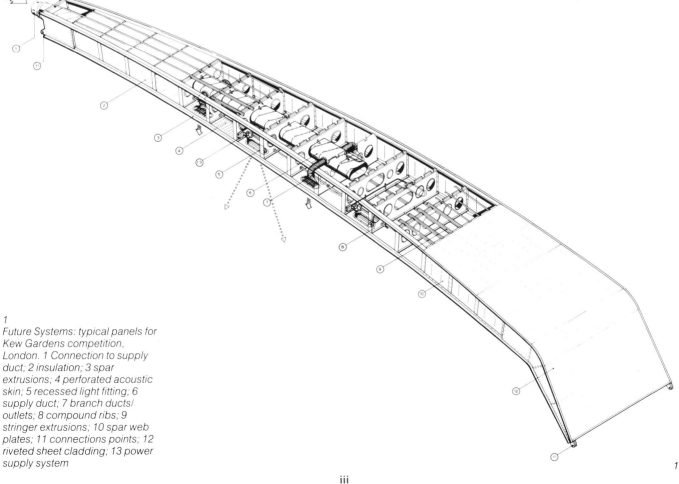

1
Future Systems: typical panels for Kew Gardens competition, London. 1 Connection to supply duct; 2 insulation; 3 spar extrusions; 4 perforated acoustic skin; 5 recessed light fitting; 6 supply duct; 7 branch ducts/ outlets; 8 compound ribs; 9 stringer extrusions; 10 spar web plates; 11 connections points; 12 riveted sheet cladding; 13 power supply system

2
Foster Associates: typical panel
fixing detail, Sainsbury Centre,
Norwich. 1 Aluminium outer skin;
2 insulation core; 3 neoprene
ladder gasket; 4 tubular steel
structural member; 5 laminated
glass; 6 enamelled extruded
aluminium subframe; 7 aluminium
inner skin; 8 nut and bolt fixing; 9
stainless steel screws; 10
stainless steel nuts and bolts; 11
aluminium channel stiffener

tions. Margaret Law at Ove Arup and Partners, for example, deals with fire-protection strategies. However, such in-house knowledge is often jealously guarded and not readily available to others in the profession seeking to undertake similar forms of construction.

Interestingly, in passing on from one practice to another staff do take their knowledge of new techniques and availability of materials with them. For example, Chris Wilkinson's detailing of the Greene King Brewery with Hopkins can be compared with similar later detailing on the Fleetguard Factory when he was with Richard Rogers (see Figures 3(a) and (b)).

Practices involved in 'high-tech' building often depend upon the knowledge of certain manufacturers with whom there is a mutual understanding of the requirements for quality control and detailing. In preparing an index of UK projects and the manufacturers of their components over recent years it is surprising how many times the names of such companies as Modern Art Glass, Tubeworkers Ltd, Spacedeck, Pirelli, Plannja or Redfern Rubber might occur.

No book on construction or case studies of cladding systems can replace the accumulated knowledge of staff in these firms of manufacturers, architects and engineers. They can, however, give an introduction to the state of the art by showing a precedent, and thus imbue confidence in architects so that they can approach a manufacturer with a reasonable working knowledge of what is feasible. This book is therefore meant as a contribution to that debate.

Building construction has been in a time of change for the last decade. Theories of prefabrication and component assembly as proposed by Wachsmann,[1] Prouvé[2] and others have come to startling reality in the works of Norman Foster and Richard Rogers. Ideas of component assembly contained in that wonderful book *The Turning Point of Building* by Wachsmann, which should be essential reading for all students of prefabrication, have been developed into new architectural forms, as shown by the work of Jan Kaplicky and David Nixon of Future Systems (Figure 1), and it is no accident that Jean Prouvé was called over for lunch at the time of the design of the Hongkong and Shanghai Bank, or that the work of Gustaf Eiffel is so prominently displayed in the entrance area at Foster's London office.

In this period of change, where there are no estab-

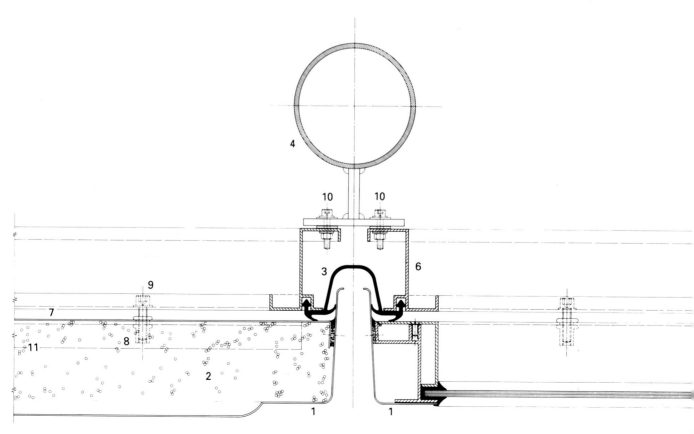

2

3
Typical cladding panel and post junction. (a) Greene King brewery, Bury St Edmunds. 1 Acrylic-coated steel cover strips; 2 steel cladding post; 3 mild steel carrier channel; 4 50 mm Rockwool insulation and vapour barrier; 5 profiled steel sheet coated externally with PVF² ; 6 profiled steel sheet, perforated and coated in white acrylic; 7 pressed steel cill flashing; 8 extruded aluminium cover strip; 9 cellular plastic profiled filler piece. (b) Fleetguard Factory, Quimper, Brittany, France. 1 Anodized aluminium top-hat section cover strip; 2 200 × 100 mm r.h.s. cladding post; 3 50 × 50 mm steel angle welded to r.h.s.; 4 60 mm thick paper-face fibreglass insulation; 5 profiled steel sheet coated with silver PVF² ; 6 cellular plastic profiled filler piece

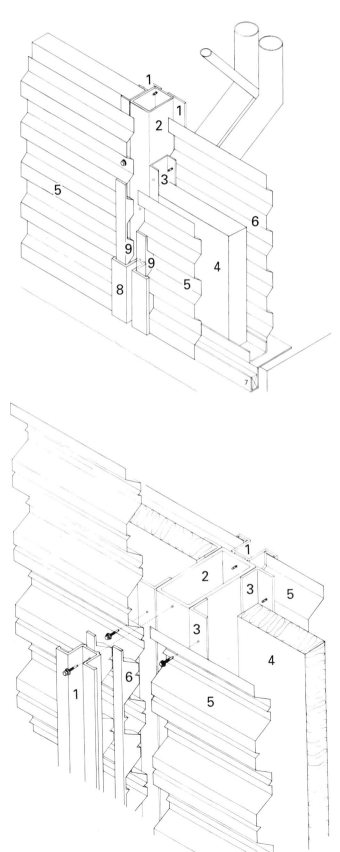

lished textbooks which discuss the issues related to newer technologies, architects and students often blindly copy details associated with the more well-known precedents. For example, how many times in schools of architecture does one see the joint detail as used at the Sainsbury Centre (Figure 2)? The authors of such copies clearly are unaware of the difficulties of manufacturing the panels or of the fabrication requirements of site vulcanizing the huge and costly neoprene net which covered the entire building and, of course, more recently of the water penetration into the phenolic cores.

More seriously for practice, British Standards, Codes of Practice and standard specifications are also not available for many of the new materials, their limitations and means of assembly. Architects are thus often forced into the dangerous circumstance of 're-inventing the wheel'.

Understandably, this situation has always existed in a period of change of building method and does so until such a time that the building industry can learn by 'sitting next to Nellie' or where designers can rely on standard pattern books as a source of inspiration and information. It is well known that the development of Renaissance architecture would not have spread so rapidly in England had it not been for Palladio's pattern books. Similarly, the introduction of the Queenpost Truss to England by Inigo Jones was widely used as a result of the description of the construction details in carpentry manuals of that time. The development of the balloon frame in America and the widespread use of cast iron for prefabricated buildings during the nineteenth century also occurred because of publication of the standard details. Such pattern books are not available for designers using today's technology.

One of the difficulties facing the author of a book on modern construction is the widespread nature of the different technologies currently available to architects. Thus a book of case studies which deals briefly with a selection of materials and assembly details can only be seen as a guide towards current trends in component assembly and not a comprehensive catalogue. Sebastyen[3] had similar difficulties in presenting available methods of lightweight building construction in 1972. His book still remains one of the best sources of pattern-book information available to students of modern lightweight building technology today.

Because of the complexity of the present building industry and the recent advances in techniques of building such as silicone glazing or tensile structures it is not surprising that even the more experienced architects lack the confidence or the information to incorporate these new methods into their designs. Hence it was easy for Pawley[4] to claim that 'Architecture is an occult world of ignorance and obsolete mystery shot through with individual acts of achievement'. That is not to say that we should agree with his conclusion that we should borrow from other industries. The skills are present within our profession, but how often is one made aware of the frustration of students unable to carry out their design ideas because of their lack of constructional knowledge, and how many good design ideas are lost as a result of what is seen as the chore of preparing working drawings? There is, or ought to be, a clear connection between design and construction in architecture. The understanding of construction should be a joy which informs design ideas. This book is intended in its small way to give at least some inspiration to designers wishing to improve their technical understanding of the newer building processes with which they are now involved and have the information available if they care to seek it.

Alan J. Brookes
Chris Grech
July 1989

References

1. Wachsmann, K., *The Turning Point of Building*, Reinhold, New York, 1961.
2. Huber, B. and Steinegger, J.C., *Jean Prouvé*, Les Editions d'Architecture Artemis, Zurich, 1971.
3. Sebastyen, G., *Lightweight Building Construction*, George Godwin, London, 1977.
4. Pawley, M., 'Technology transfer', *Architectural Review*, No. 1087, September 1987, pp. 31–39.

Further reading

Klotz, H., *Vision der Moderne*, Prestel Verlag, Munich, 1986.
Russel, B., *Building Systems, Industrialisation and Architecture*, John Wiley, Chichester, 1981.

Inspiration for this book also came from:

Ackermann, K., *Industriebau*, Deutsche Verlags-Anstalt, Stuttgart, 1984.
Buckminster Fuller, R., *Inventions – the Patented Works of R. Buckminster Fuller*, St Martin's Press, New York, 1983.
Griffoen, A., *Techniek in Bouw en Industrie*, Stichting Bouwresearch, Rotterdam, 1984.
Ogg, A., *Architecture in Steel – the Australian Context*, Royal Australian Institute of Architects, 1987.
Pegrum, R., *Details in Australian Architecture*, RAIE Education, 1984.

Acknowledgements

During the preparation of this book we were both very busy in private practice, thus without the constant prodding from our research assistant, Rebecca Cavell, this project could not have been completed. Thanks must also go to our typist, Marylynn Fyvie-Gauld, for her willing smiles and late-night stints on the word processor and the additional help received from Debi Wallace. Thanks also to Jackie and family for their continuous support.

Many colleagues have also offered helpful advice with the various case studies, and in particular we would like to thank Mike Stacey for his collaboration on a number of articles, including the *AJ Focus* series on 'Cladding and Curtain Walling', on which the Introduction to this book is based. Our thanks also to Chris Wilkinson, Jim Eyre, Mick Eekhout, Michael Cohen, Tony Hunt, Spencer de Grey, John Silver, John Thornton and Mark Goldstein. Kind assistance was also provided by Shirley McPherson at the *Architects' Journal* and Pauline Shirley at Ove Arup and Partners by giving us access to their photographic libraries and by Alan Ogg for drawings from his own book. Our thanks also go to the various students and colleagues who helped us with the preparation of the drawings, especially Kim Ng, Lucas Murphy, Manfred Huber, Christian Huber and Jerry Metcalfe.

Photographic credits

Ahrends Burton & Koralek, 24.1
Arup Associates, 11.2, 11.4, 11.6, 11.7
Asselbergs, T., 18.1, 18.5, 18.10
Atelier Piano, 12.5
Bailey, R.P., 28.2
Baitz, O., 22.1, 22.4, 22.5, 22.6, 23.6
Bell & Partners, 21.1, 21.2, 21.3, 21.4, 21.5, 21.6, 21.7, 21.8
Benthem Crouwel Architekten BNA, 2.7
Bower, D., 25.9
Boyd, R., 15.8
Brock Carmichael Associates, 15.7

Brookes, A.J., Intro 3, 1.4, 1.6, 2.3, 2.6 5.1, 5.6, 5.7, 9.1, 9.2, 9.10, 9.11, 9.12(a), 9.12(b) 12.9, 12.10, 13.2, 14.3, 14.6(a), 18.9, 29.2 29.3, 29.4
Bryant, R., Intro 1, 16.1, 16.5, 26.2, 26.7, 31.2, 31.11
Charles, M., 2.1, 14.1
Childs, N., 21.7
Clarke, C., 5.2
Cook, P., 4.3, 4.4, 4.5, 4.7, 6.2, 6.5, 6.11, 14.5, 24.4
De Backer & Associates, 11.5
Eekhout, M., 1.1
Foster Associates, Pref. 2, 27.1, 27.2, 27.3, 27.4, 27.5, 27.6, 27.7, 27.8, 27.9, 32.2, 32.4, 32.8, 32.9
Future Systems, Pref. 1
Gibson, K., 3.1, 3.2, 3.5
Grad Hillier Partnership, 23.1
Grech, C., 8.1, 8.3, 8.4, 8.5, 14.6(b), 25.1, 25.5
Hannay, P., 12.8
Horden, R., 30.2, 30.3, 30.4, 30.5, 30.9
Hoyt, W/Esto., 19.2
Integration AP, Intro 4
King D/McAlister R., 33.1, 33.2, 33.3, 33.4, 33.5, 33.6, 33.7, 33.8, 33.9
Kirkwood, K., 30.10
Lambot, I., 32.1, 32.5, 32.6
McKenna, S., 5.2
Michael Hopkins & Partners, 25.2
Mills, J. Photography Ltd, 15.1
Nye, J., 32.3, 32.7
Ogg, A., 9.3, 9.4, 9.5, 9.6, 9.7, 9.8, 9.9
Picardi, G., 7.2, 7.3, 7.4, 7.5, 7.6, 7.7, 7.8, 7.9, 7.10
Richard Rogers & Partners, 14.4, 14.7, 14.8
Sharp, D., 1.3
Stoller, E . Esto., 13.1
Studio 70, 28.28.3
Theodorov, S., 6.6
Vanden Bosche J., 20.2, 20.4
Vanderwarker, P., 10.1
Wilson, G., 6.3
Young, J., 14.2
Ove Arup & Partners, 12.1, 12.5, 12.7, 16.1, 16.5, 22.1, 22.4, 22.5, 22.6

Introduction

Cladding and its frame

Although intended as a book of technology with case-study examples, inevitably there is a concentration of information here concerning cladding, as this, as part of the building envelope, is often the most critical element of building construction in so much that it affects its exterior appearance and keeps the weather out.

Non-loadbearing cladding in building, often in panel form, is most commonly used in conjunction with a structural framework. Since the example of the Crystal Palace, where prefabricated components combined with a long-span cast iron structure resulted in a rapidly constructed and elegant exhibition hall, architects have appreciated the benefits of standardization of components for fitting within a framed assembly.

Clearly, the frame necessary to support the cladding can be either steel or concrete. The concept for an early concrete frame building, designed by Le Corbusier, is the Domino House. Le Corbusier was one of the first architects to exploit and popularize the idea that buildings could be freed from the constraints of loadbearing construction. The idea was that a wall only needs to support itself, and therefore could be all glass or the doorway in any position desired. The spanning capacity of the panel becomes a determining factor in the formation of the building and its planning grid.

However, it is only in the last 15 to 20 years that buildings such as Aztec West, near Bristol, have been constructed, taking full advantage of frame construction (Figure 1). Here the envelope of the building becomes fully interchangeable: doors (even loading-bay doors) can be relocated, windows combined with insulated panels or louvres exchanged with windows. The possibilities of combination are considerable and the technology to achieve this is now readily available. Strict modular coordination is essential to make it possible. Dimensional control linked with controlled sizing of accurately made machine-produced panels allow panels or louvres to be replaced over the life of the building.

Clients and contractors often perceive the main advantage of prefabrication as being the speed of erection, thus minimizing the time spent on site, realizing the potential of the investment and allowing early occupation of the building. To this has been added the concept of fast-track construction where the architect and other consultants working with a project manager design the final form and components of the building during the construction process, thus minimizing the lead time. Lloyds of London designed by the Richard Rogers Partnership, and Darling Habour in Sydney, by Philip Cox and Partners, both included as case studies in this book,

1

are excellent examples where prefabricated components (including cladding panels) and fast-track contract management have produced a contemporary image using precision in manufacture and assembly with appropriate technology.

Composite metal panel

Many materials can be used for cladding, e.g. precast concrete, profiled metal, GRP, GRC and curtain walling (see Brookes, *Cladding of Buildings*). However, it is the use of composite panels and, in particular, composite metal panels which are now in increasing use for all types of buildings.

This increase is partly due to the introduction of improved insulation, thus leading to the development of composite insulated panels and overcladding systems. It is also a factor of the desire to reduce the amount of support framework by increasing the spanning performance of composite panels. In this way spans of 3–5 m can be achieved compared to 1.5–2.5 m with single-sheet profiled material. Use of sandwich panels with their self-finished interior and exterior skins can also show definite advantages in speed of assembly provided that the method of fixing allows efficient placing of the units which, being lightweight, can normally be handled by two men.

Composite construction is now a familiar principle in products as diverse as tennis racquets and jet aircraft. In building, this principle is applied to cladding panels whereby two sheets of metal are held apart by core material to which both sheets are bonded. It is the spacing of the two metal sheets which is predominantly responsible for the rigidity of the final composite. Basically, the wider the spacing, the greater the spanning capabilities of the finished product.

The benefits of composite construction are:

1. Light weight;
2. Long span (longer than profiled single sheet metal, i.e. for the identical load criteria: a typical profiled sheet spans 1.5 m – a composite spans 4 m);
3. Provision of insulation – if core selected, it has an insulation performance (e.g. polystyrene or polyurethane foam);
4. A combination of the advantages of different materials;
5. Accurate manufacture in factory conditions which leads to precise appearance/image;
6. Fast erection time – direct-result, large-size accuracy of manufacture;
7. It is self-finished inside and out – it only requires a frame and it is a complete building envelope;
8. Flexibility – its lightness facilitates relocation and even replacement.

One of the first examples of metal composite cladding was designed by Jean Prouvé for the Maison du Peuple at Clichy, outside Paris (Figure 2), completed in 1939. It is important to note the thermally broken joint and that the asbestos-lined steel sheet skins are kept apart by a spring. This is an early use of composite construction.

Despite the clarity of Prouvé's early projects and his other pioneering work in this field (for example, the development of the use of aluminium extrusions), it is surprising that composite cladding panels only became available as commercial systems in the 1970s. In England there were very few composite panel systems (e.g. the Oxford Regional Hospital Board), whereas by the end of the 1970s the market was bristling with diverse composite panel systems such as Metecno, Hoesch, Crawford Doors, H.H. Robertson, Modern Art Glass, Hunter Douglas and Booth-Muirie, among others.

The major turning point in the 1970s can be considered to be the energy crisis of 1973, which led to a realization that there was an essential need to conserve energy. Thus the thermal performance of the building envelope became much more important, and this, in turn, led to a greater concern for insulation and insulated panels.

The importance of the Sainsbury Centre design by Foster Associates in 1977 lies partly in the fact that it was new technology and that it incorporated interchangeable components. It was one of the first uses of Superplastic Aluminium for insulated composite cladding panels, but, more importantly, it was one of the first non-commercial, non-industrial buildings (it is an art gallery) to use an interchangeable panel system. It is a building which has gained an international reputation and has stimulated the development of component-based architecture throughout the world. Identical 1.8 × 1.2 m panels were used for both walls and roof, and the joint detail depends upon the neoprene gasket being mounted back against an aluminium carrier system.

Sadly, perhaps because this was such an early example of the application of these principles, the original panels have had to be replaced by flat white ones manufactured in the USA by Cupples Product Division of H.H. Robertson, which has transformed the aesthetic appearance of the building.

One of the disadvantages of being ahead of the state of the art in building is that all the characteristics of the construction may not be known at the time of the design. In this case, it is said that moisture inherent within the phenolic foam has built up, causing corrosion on the panels leading to their replacement.

A more recent application of aluminium panels in the UK is illustrated by the Herman Miller extension at

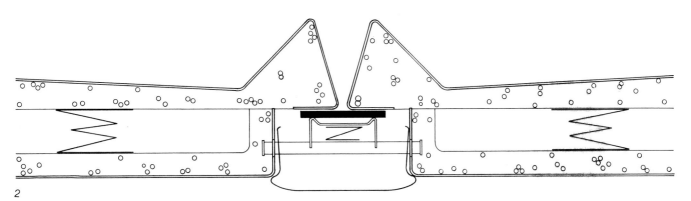

2

Chippenham (Figure 3) (architect: Nicholas Grimshaw), where 2.4 × 1.2 m pressed aluminium panels were mounted onto a series of back-to-back 'Unistrut sections', using fixings expressed on the surface of the panel. The detail incorporates a large-section neoprene gasket used vertically. A decorative T-section in contrasting colour is used to hide the horizontal joint. This system has now been developed by Grimshaw on such projects as Sainsbury Camden Town and the Financial Times Print Works.

Types of assembly

Essentially, there are three types of panel assemblies:

1. *Panel-to-subframe assembly*, whereby the panels are jointed by subframe curtain walling carrier systems, normally in aluminium, which is, in turn, fixed back to the main framing;
2. *Panel-to-panel assembly*, whereby panels are jointed to each other and fixed directly back to the main structure or secondary framing;
3. *Rainscreen panels*, whereby an outer panel provides a weather shield to the insulated inner one. As the name 'screen' suggests, these panels are only a first-stage barrier.

Panel-to-subframe assemblies

Here, steel- or aluminium-faced panels, with either laminated or foamed insulation cores, are mounted onto a curtain walling type subframe using structural gaskets. The perceived advantage of the panel-to-subframe assembly is that it offers the opportunity of interchangeable window/wall panels with a similar joint on all four sides of the panel.

There are many UK manufacturers offering proprietary systems of this nature, including Astrawall, Modern Art Glass and Don Reynolds Ltd. With panel-to-subframe assemblies in particular, the cross-over junction of horizontal and vertical joints is critical for weathertightness. The method of connecting the mullions and transoms and the tolerances of cutting aluminium sections and their assembly is critical to achieve a water- and airtight joint.

An example from practice where small, 1 × 1.8 m panels, are mounted into an aluminium frame is at Benson Electronics at Aztec West, near Bristol (architect: Brian Taggart). Here the cladding is a chequerboard of interchangeable panels. These are finished in polyester powder coating and have a 40 mm layer of ('Styrofoam' bonded to the inner face (see Brookes, *Concepts of Cladding*

3

4

A development of this principle, using a lattice grid of EPDM gasket similar to that designed for the Sainsbury Centre, was adopted for the construction of the new Gatwick Airport North Piers. In this case a special requirement for sound insulation led to the aluminium being laminated onto a core of cement-based chipboard to increase the density of the panel. After foaming and prior to lamination to their cores the skins were coated with Silver 'Duranar' PVF^2. Another example included here is the case study on Benthem and Crouwel's Customs House (Case Study 8).

Panel-to-panel assemblies

Here, the panels are linked together, often incorporating a secret fixing within the joint. Various types of joints are possible between panels, including:

- Tongue and groove details;
- Overlap details;
- Compressed seals using continuous channels;
- Face-applied gasket systems;
- Top-hat sections.

Although most proprietary panel-to-panel systems have windows mounted within the panel it is also possible to provide a window-to-panel solution by means of a third member or jointing piece. The horizontal and vertical joints will be different, thus offering less interchangeability. Panel-to-panel assemblies, particularly those using tongue and groove joints, normally rely on sequential stacking. If panels have to be replaced due to damage they are best arranged in bays.

Panel-to-panel systems are now being developed which allow windows and doors to be assembled directly to the panel. The envelope by Integration RVP for ICI at Macclesfield using steel-faced panels with a microprofiled surface illustrates this principle (Figure 7).

With careful detailing it is possible to install panel-to-panel assemblies vertically, horizontally or a combination of both. The 'Styrospan' system recently developed by the author with Dow Chemical Australia achieves a cross-over joint using a variety of panel profiles. This system has recently been used at the National Tennis Centre in Melbourne.

Rainscreen panels

This type of system depends upon an outer layer of flat metal sheet approximately 4–6 mm thick mounted in front of laminated panels with a ventilated cavity between the two parts of the construction. These sheets, usually butt jointed, offer a first protection against driving rain (rainscreen). The panels behind provide the thermal and acoustic performance and can be mounted into a carrier system or fixed to secondary framing as in previous examples.

Small butt joints between panels are possible using this method. Provided that an adequate external-grade lining can be attached to the outside face of the laminated panel then the size of the panel is only limited to the maximum size of the plate panel and its ability to span between supports. The gauge of the plate panel must be such as to avoid rippling and distortion of the sheet.

Rainscreen panel systems are increasingly being used as a method of upgrading existing facades, particularly for high-rise buildings erected in the UK in the 1960s and now in need of repair or improved external insulation. A recent example is Parsons House (architect: Peter Bell and Partners), where aluminium panels by Schmidlin are mounted using pins onto vertical aluminium carriers on the facade of the building (see Case Study 21).

Finishes for cladding

Various finishes are available:

1. Silicone-modified polyester (SMP);
2. Fluorocarbon (PVF^2);
3. Stainless steel;
4. Anodized aluminium.

Stainless steel, as used at the stair and service cores at the Lloyds Building in London, is very expensive. Anodized aluminium is costly and it is very difficult to achieve colour match, as any variation in alloy or time in the anodizing bath will cause colour variation. Generally speaking, the pre-painted steel sheet finishes will offer better colour ranges and are cheaper. However, their durability beyond 15 years cannot be guaranteed. All paint finishes are affected to some degree by ultraviolet light and will fade with time. PVF^2 has the best colour stability but its coat (25 microns) needs protection during assembly of panels on site. Touch-up paints are available for minor scratches.

Testing and quality control

Architects should request evidence from manufacturers that their products fully satisfy the performance requirements in the form of test data. With integrated systems, the manufacturers are now taking on responsibility for the complete envelope. This leads to a requirement for more adequate testing of not only the parts but also the combination of the individual components.

Manufacturers should only offer fully tested solutions, but this, unfortunately, is not always the case. Many systems on offer are under-resolved, almost like second-generation prototypes rather than completely designed and developed products.

In common with all manufactured products, quality control is vital to ensure satisfactory completion of the facades. Architects should not just seek compliance with British Standards but must also be prepared to ask manufacturers for evidence of their quality-control procedures and to monitor them at intervals as the job progresses (see BS 5750, Quality Systems as a starting point).

A further difficulty is that cladding technology has outpaced the production of British Standards, and architects can no longer solely rely on BS specifications covering particular systems. Areas falling outside the scope of British Standards should be adequately covered by the project-performance specification.

Thus the development of panel systems together with many components used in modern construction demands an increased dialogue between architects, manufacturers and contractors on such issues as fixing and jointing techniques, types of finishes and quality control on sites. Poor control of detailing will spoil the effect of the best panel production. It is essential that architects join with manufacturers to discuss the details for any particular project, and, where possible, they should seek tenders from those manufacturers who offer a complete design fabrication and installation service to ensure a quality product.

Finally, a good building is dependent on its detailing. The architect must control the size of the joints and the location of flashings to ensure the fine quality required for component assembly.

The built work of many of the architects shown in this book clearly displays their interest in technology and their ability to take a positive role in taking advantage of technological advances and informing the process of construction.

References

Architects' Journal, 'The art of construction – sheet metal cladding', 8 July 1981, pp. 78–85; 15 July 1981, pp. 121–126.

Architects' Journal, 'Products in practice – cladding', Special supplement, 31 July 1985.

Architects' Journal, 'Element design guide – metal panels', Special supplement, 6 August 1986, pp. 39–44.

Brookes, A.J., *Cladding of Buildings*, Construction Press, London, 1983.

Brookes, A.J., *Concepts in Cladding*, Construction Press, London, 1985.

Contents

The Bandstand at Haarlem
Architect
Wiek Roling with Mick Eekhout

1.1.

1.1.
General view of bandstand

1.2.
Basic Tuball node without glazing. 1 Special aluminium casting of main body of node; 2 aluminium casting of top of node bolted down to main body; 3 tubular member with end plate drilled and threaded to fit onto bolt projecting from node

1.3.
Bruno Taut's 1914 Glass House

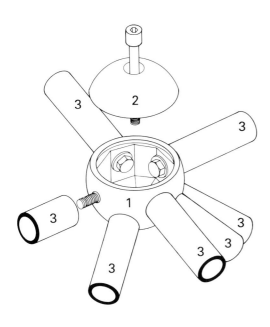

1.2.

1.3.

General

This small music pavilion at Haarlem in Holland (Figure 1.1), which was the winner of a limited competition, has been included here not only for its elegant design, standing on ten fixed pillars on a podium, but also because it demonstrates clearly how a glazed panel can be fitted to a space frame construction. This is a detail requirement which often puzzles students of architecture attempting to fix external panels to a space frame where the nodes clearly are required to project above and below the tubular space-frame connectors.

The other factor to note in this case is the detail of the node itself, with no bolts or nuts to distract the eye. The only visible elements are spherical cast aluminium nodes and extruded aluminium tubular bars, all painted in white, with the glazing between (Figure 1.2).

Inevitably, some comparison must be made with Bruno Taut's Glass House for the Werkbund Exhibition at Cologne of 1914 (Figure 1.3), possibly because of the proportions of the columns to dome or the relationship of the diamond-shaped glass panels. In the case of the Bandstand, however, these diamond shapes are produced with two sheets of triangular glazing with a round rather than pointed dome. It is here that the similarities of construction end. The intention, however, in both cases was to achieve a building with standardized components, and the Bandstand can be seen as a modern example of the latest glazing techniques in the same way that Taut's Glass House promoted the use of glass and therefore the German glass industries that paid for it.

Structure

The structure comprises 10 steel columns with fixed connections to a tubular steel perimeter member serrated to form a semi-hexagonal edge (Figure 1.4) on which the Tuball-type space frame by Octatube is supported. This space frame comprises an extruded aluminium bar which also acts to support the glazing above. This is cunningly cut back at its connection with the nodes (formed by using aluminium castings) so that the form of the castings become visually apparent to the observer (Figure 1.5). The triangular glazed sections (originally designed as polycarbonate) are fixed to the glazing member by an aluminium plate with external bolt connections (Figure 1.6).

It is perhaps unfortunate that the glazing has suffered so much from vandalism, and therefore subsequent re-sealing of this plating member has led to a more untidy condition of the corner plate connections than had no re-sealing been necessary.

References

Eekhout, M., 'An architectural generation of space structures', Paper, First Internat. Conf. on Lightweight Structures in Architecture, Sydney, Australia, August 1986, published by Unisearch Ltd, University of NSW (August 1986), pp. 96–103.

Eekhout, M., 'Het vormgeven van aluminium tot ruimtelijke contructies', Alutech Conf., Utrecht, Feb. 1988.

Eekhout, M., 'Architecture in space structures', PhD thesis, Delft, 1989.

Millfield Library
College of Technology
BELFAST

1.4.
Tubular steel columns supporting
a serrated perimeter edge beam

1.5.
Tuball glazed space frame node.
1 Spherical aluminium casting; 2
aluminium struts extruded with
flange to take glazing assembly,
cut away at node; 3 glazing; 4
cover plate

1.6.
Aluminium cover plates with
external bolt fixings

1.4.

1.6.

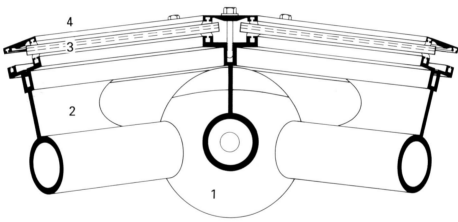

1.5.

2

Benthem and Crouwel's House at Almere
Architects
Benthem and Crouwel

2.1. General view

General

Built on a site in Almere, a new town near Amsterdam, Holland, this design was one of 10 prizewinning entries for a 1982 open-brief competition requiring a structure capable of being dismantled and removed from the site after five years. The prize was the use of the site within that time (Figure 2.1).

Benthem and Crouwel's design attempts to disturb the site as little as possible by resting the modular house on a proprietary steel space frame which is supported at four points on precast concrete industrial flooring slabs. The house is designed to minimal space standards and is planned on a 2 m grid derived from the length (2 m) of a bunk bed (Figure 2.2). Two bedrooms are arranged either side of the kitchen and bathroom, all grouped along one wall of the building. These form the 'solid' part of the walls, while remaining space is taken by the entirely glazed living space with a balcony leading from it.

The glazing is structural, supporting the roof which is flat. The brief of the competition required only structural stability and fire regulations to be adhered to. Benthem and Crouwel decided to use lightweight, low-cost, high-performance materials to enable the building to be demountable and relocated.

The space frame

The space frame is a proprietary steel frame by Octatube (Delft) with octagonal connectors at 2 m centres (Figure 2.3). The struts of the frame are 50 mm diameter tubular steel with flattened ends bolted to connecting plate formed by a 5 mm thick octagonal steel plate. The space frame is connected to four precast concrete industrial flooring slabs, 2 m square, 160 mm deep, placed directly on the ground. In order to allow levelling and for settlement adjustment the fixing plates are connected with thick steel plates, with a sleeved joint which prevents

5

2.2.
(a) Plan. 1 Bedroom; 2 kitchen; 3
bathroom; 4 living room; 5 heat
exchanger; 6 underfloor heating
ducts; 7 balcony; 8 sliding door.
(b) Section. 1 Living room ; 2
bathroom; 3 heat exchanger; 4
insulated supply ducts to
perimeter grilles; 5 services entry
point

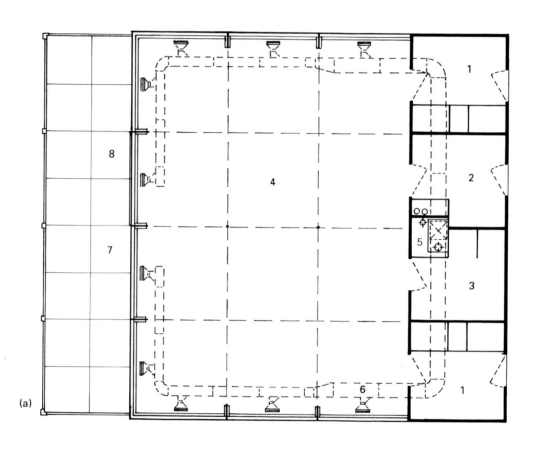

(a)

2.2.   (b)

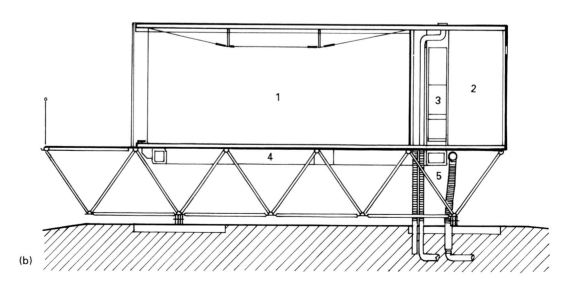

2.3.
Octagonal space frame connectors

2.4.
Sleeved space frame support detail. 1 Precast concrete base; 2 levelling bolts; 3 sleeved circular hollow sections; 4 octagonal space frame connector; 5 flattened tube struts

lateral movement but allows vertical adjustment using four bolts fixed to the slabs with chemical anchors (Figure 2.4).

The floor

The floor decking consists of a sandwich panel of 5 mm plywood on a 30 mm high-density polyurethane foam core bolted directly to the space-frame substructures. The upper chord members of the space frame are omitted, the sandwich floor acting as an upper chord allowing the integration of bending and compression forces. To prevent sagging of the floor above the space frame, 37 × 67 mm timber battens were bonded to the upper face of the panels at 400 mm centres and a further skin of 18 mm plywood screwed to them (total thickness, 95 mm). The balcony was made from steel industrial floor gratings, bolted directly to the space frame.

2.3.

Solid wall panels

The solid panels forming bedroom, bathroom and kitchen walls are made of a sandwich of 5 mm skins of plywood either side of a 30 mm core of high-density polyurethane foam (Figure 2.9).

Glazed walls

The walls of the main living space are made of 12 mm thick toughened glass with 15 mm thick glass-stabilizing fins which prevents the glass from bending under wind pressure and also restrains the perimeter of the roof. The interesting feature of this particular construction is the use of silicone glazing joints and fixing cleats between the sheets of glass, producing an elegant detail without the use of window framing.

The glass fins were restrained by aluminium brackets screwed to the floor and the roof was fixed to the fins by the same means, using M10 bolts in nylon bushes. In addition, aluminium corner brackets (functional for 4 days only until the silicone corner joints cure and become structural) were fitted between the fins and the glass walls (Figure 2.5). (This technique was later developed by Benthem and Crouwel for the exhibition building at Sonsbeek, Arnhem, in 1986 (Figure 2.7), where neither intermediate nor corner cleats were used.)

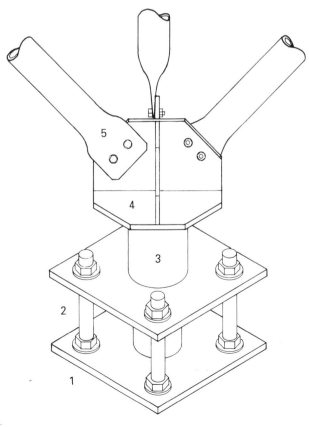

2.4.

2.5.
Details of glass-stabilizing fins. 1 12 mm thick toughened glass sheets; 2 15 mm thick toughened glass fins; 3 aluminium brackets bolted down to floor (three M10 bolts secure the glass fin); 4 glass sheet slotted into 30 × 20 mm steel channel and sealed with silicone sealant; 5 glass countersunk to take countersunk bolts fixed to intermediate aluminium corner cleats; 6 aluminium bracket bolted to roof deck, restraining head of fin

2.6.
Underfloor ductwork and flexible drainage hoses

2.7.
Oblique view of sculpture pavilion, Arnhem

2.7.

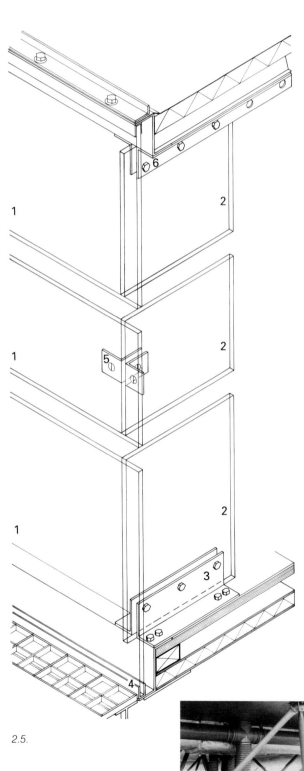

2.5.

2.6.

The roof

The roof deck is 0.75 mm thick corrugated steel sheet, waterproofed by a 1 mm thick EPDM membrane loose laid without falls in a single piece with interim fixing clips (Figure 2.8) on 50 mm 'Styrofoam' insulation board. The roof deck was reinforced by trusses formed from perforated mild steel angles with 8 mm diameter stainless steel tensioning wires (Figure 2.2). In addition, because the roof was so lightweight it was necessary to tie it down to the floor deck with two stainless steel tensioning wires inside the building. At the perimeter the trusses are bolted to the glass-stabilizing fins and are thus restrained at their edges.

Sequence of assembly

Thus the overall sequence of assembly as shown in Figure 2.10 was:

1. Place foundation slabs;
2. Fix space frame to slabs;
3. Place floor slabs and balcony;
4. Fix solid wall panels;
5. Fix glazed panels and fins;
6. Fix roof trusses and tension rods;
7. Place roof deck;
8. Finish roof deck.

Services

Connection to the underground drainage and mains water supply is by flexible hose. Heating is by heat exchanger fed from a district heating system distributed through the house by underfloor ducts (see Figure 2.2). Electrical supply is from sockets located at ceiling height, switched manually or by remote control from the central control unit.

The air-conditioning ducts are insulated and suspended from below the floor deck (Figure 2.6). A single rainwater outlet is carried through partition walls to drains below.

References

Anon., 'Dutch courage', *Architects' Journal* (building feature), 7 August 1985, pp. 30–34.

Berni, L. and Leroy, A., 'Holland: a constructive workshop', *Ottagono*, March 1987, pp. 20–33.

Buchanan, P., 'High-tech and high style', *Architectural Review*, January 1985, pp. 56–57.

Buchanan, P., 'Barely there – sculpture pavilion at Arnhem', *Architectural Review*, September 1987, pp. 81–84.

2.8.
Section through roof fixing. 1
0.75 mm thick corrugated metal
sheeting; 2 50 mm 'Styrofoam'
insulation board; 3 locating
washer fixed to steel decking with
self-tapping screws; 4 1 mm
EPDM membrane; 5 push-fit inner
sealing clip; 6 screw-down
sealing cap

2.9.
Method of fixing external panels.
1 Steel Z angle (25 × 50 ×
25 mm); 2 perimeter angle (50 ×
20 mm) bolted to Z angle; 3
sealant joint; 4 cover strip angle
(30 × 70 mm) riveted to panel; 5
40 mm polyurethane foam/
plywood composite panel; 6 30 ×
90 mm batten glued to panel; 7

panels fixed to Z angle with coach
screws; 8 EPDM membrane laid
loose on 50 mm extruded
polystyrene fixed to profiled steel
roof decking; 9 18 mm plywood
flooring screwed to 37 × 67 mm
timber battens bonded to upper
face of composite panels

2.10.
Sequence of assembly

2.8.

2.10.

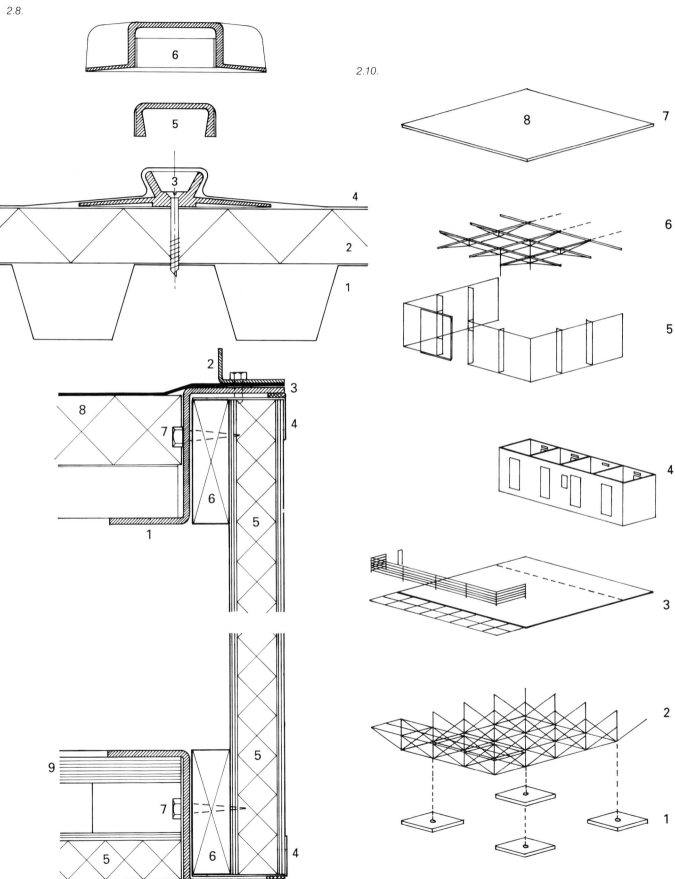

2.9.

9

3

The Burrell Gallery, Glasgow
Architects
Barry Gasson

General

The Burrell Gallery was built in 1983 as the winner of a competition to design a structure to house the Sir William Burrell Collection, which was bequeathed to the city of Glasgow in 1944 (Figure 3.2). This museum uses a wide variety of environmental control technology to enable it to protect its exhibits from pollution and damaging sunlight while at the same time being largely glazed to command views of the surrounding woodland, therefore placing the collection in the rural setting Burrell desired.

Traditionally built mainly in a variety of materials, the structure incorporates parts of the collection such as carved stone doors and windows into its own fabric, so that visitors walk through the doorways and experience them more fully and closely than they would had they been exhibited as objects simply to look at (Figure 3.1).

No overall grid governs the design: rather, each space is individually considered according to the particular exhibits' requirements. The spaces are then unified by the use of materials, which is a language of concrete columns, natural timber and stone and glass throughout. Gasson collaborated closely with James R. Briggs and Associates (environmental control system designers) from the start, to create a building specifically geared towards the ideal maintenance and display conditions its exhibits require.

3.1.

Structure

The architects have refined the structure to a point of simplicity, and the elegance of the junctions between its parts can only be admired. The tall 400 mm diameter concrete columns that still bear the two casting marks from the glassfibre moulds support a variety of laminated timber roof members manufactured by Kingston Craftsmen 1981 by means of bolted galvanized mild steel connector plates (Figure 3.3).

In the restaurant area and stained-glass gallery, 500 × 210 mm laminated timber perimeter beams are bolted to the columns using galvanized mild steel connector plates. These steel connections also support the rafters (105 × 333 mm) that are connected to vertical mullions of the same material and dimension by halving joints with glued and bolted timber connectors. The rafters are connected at their head to the perimeter beam by means of a galvanized mild steel T-shoe, bolted to the beam and rafter, and the mullion-to-floor junction is made by a flush-fitting mild steel shoe bolted to the concrete floor slab. The mullions and rafters are braced together by

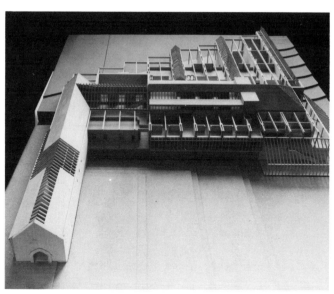

3.2.

3.1.
View along gallery to woods beyond

3.1.
*View along gallery to woods
beyond*

3.2.
*Model showing overall massing of
gallery*

3.3.
*Steel connector plates. 1 Primary
laminated timber beam (767 ×
210 mm) supported on steel plate
connector bolted to 400 mm
diameter concrete column; 2
laminated timber roof joists (267
× 105 mm); 3 motorized vertical
external aluminium roller blinds; 4
24 mm thick double glazing; 5
laminated timber perimeter beam
(500 × 210 mm); 6 laminated
timber rafter/mullion (333 ×
105 mm); 7 steel plate connector
bolted to beam and columns*

3.4.
*Horizontal glazing joint. (a)
Original design, (b) refined and
simplified joint*

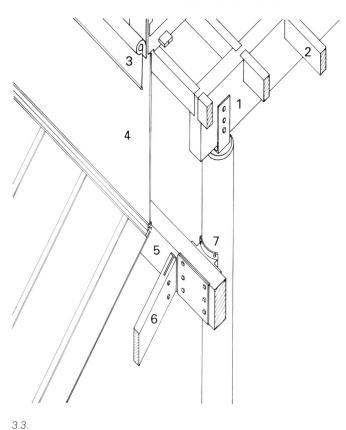

3.3.

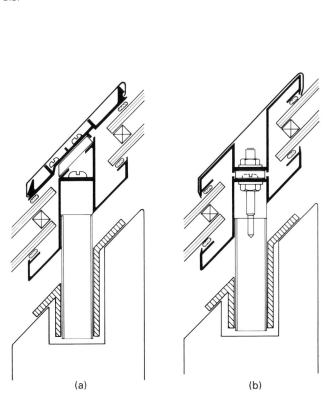

(a)   (b)

3.4.

means of mild steel tie bars.

An interesting feature of the glazing is the patent glazing bar detail to the angled restaurant wall. Gasson has refined the design so that one aluminium extrusion is used in the final design whereas initially two were required (Figure 3.4). It is this level of refinement that gives this building its great simplicity, as do the steel connector plates to the column heads which hold the laminated timber rafters away from the concrete columns.

Environmental control system

The Burrell Gallery employs a wide variety of environmental control devices. In order to control temperature and humidity, the building has been divided into 22 zones, each with its own air-handling plant. Each zone thus reacts independently to its location, environmental requirements according to function (restaurant, exhibition spaces, restorers' rooms, courtyard, etc.) and number of occupants. The system is designed to maintain 19°C ⊀ 10°C with a relative humidity of 60% + 5% where there are exhibits, with slightly higher temperatures in 'people' spaces, such as the lecture theatre. Running costs are substantially reduced by limiting fresh air intake for the six air changes per hour required to 12–31 m^3 per second, with the double-glazing seals being very efficient and heat from lighting and other incidental heat sources also being recovered.

The Burrell Gallery has been described as a giant-sized showcase with a system of blinds acting as the cover-cloth. External blinds on the south-facing glazing are operated by a push button from inside the gallery when the lighting level exceeds the recommended maximum (Figure 3.5). The blinds (PVC-covered glass fibre) can shade both vertical and sloping glazed faces. The sloping face blinds are on extruded aluminium rollers on cast aluminium brackets fixed with stainless steel pins through glazing bars to the laminated timber rafters. The blind rail travels on pulleys along stainless steel cables, with the last blind, being motorized, controlling all the others. In the vertical glazing areas the extruded aluminium blind roller brackets are fixed back to the fascia by stainless steel pins. External awnings over office spaces provide a controllable shading device, while internal blinds on the east-facing glazing provide the necessary control there. Thus, because the museum has opened itself up to the environment it has to employ an array of protective devices to prevent the damaging effects of that environment.

3.5.
External view of restaurant and
stained-glass gallery

3.5.

Costs

In this type of building, services contribute a large amount towards the total costs. In this case over 42% of the total costs was for services, with ventilation accounting for 22.7%. The structure itself – including all partitions, doors and ironmongery as well as the frame and walls – accounted for 23.2%.

References

Anon., 'The Burrell Tour', *Architects' Journal*, 19 October 1983, pp. 65–70.

Anon., 'The Burrell Tour', *Architects' Journal*, 19 October 1983, pp. 81–85.

Brawne, M., 'The Burrell museum machine', *Architects' Journal*, 19 October 1983, pp. 86–93.

Bugg, V., 'The Burrell costs/credits', *Architects' Journal*, 19 October 1983, pp. 97–98.

Glancy, J., 'The Burrell – art and architecture', *Architectural Review*, February 1984, pp. 28–37.

4

Boyatt Wood Hostel for the Disabled
Architects
Hampshire County Council Architects'
Department: (David White)

General

This hostel for physically disabled young people is situated in Selbourne Drive, Boyatt Wood, Eastleigh, in Hampshire. It was designed by David White of Hampshire County Council Architects' Department (County Architect: Colin Stansfield Smith) for Hampshire County Council Social Services Department, Raglan Housing Association. It provides six sheltered flats intended for permanent occupation and 24 bedsitting rooms grouped in fives and sixes around shared dining and sitting areas. Staff accommodation, a hairdressing service, bar, work-

The accommodation is housed in units of loadbearing brickwork construction with flat roofs providing sound and heat insulation. The 'umbrella' of PVC above it provides rain-shelter, but it is not sealed at the edges or gable ends; instead these remain open to guard against excessive heat gain within the building (Figure 4.5).

The flats/bedsitting units

These are constructed of a golden buff-coloured brick, which is also used (this time without mortar) to form the floor covering of the arcade. Doors from each unit relate

4.1. General view

shop and recharge station for wheelchair batteries are all provided. This accommodation is arranged around a central 'street', and a lightweight profiled PVC roof on light steel frame spans the entire space (Figure 4.1), reaching out at the east and west sides of the small 'town' to provide sheltered gardens and carports. The complex deliberately attempts to avoid the institutionalized corridor, and instead provides a meandering street, liberally planted, which runs from north to south with a central entrance from the west next to the communal 'forum', which forms a centrepiece in the arcade (Figures 4.2(a) and (b)). The trelliswork forming the walls and ceilings in this area is echoed in the furniture, designed by David Morriss and built by a local disabled persons' workshop (Figure 4.4).

into the central street arcade, with porches of the same brick jutting into the street. Clerestories provide additional light into the living rooms of the flats and bedsit groups.

The roof

The roofing material is carried on a frame of circular hollow section mild steel finished in a white paint. Five triangular cross-section lattice trusses run from north to south, supported at 6 m centres on the brick loadbearing walls of the accommodation below. The trusses are braced together in the line of the gable walls and also diagonally in the plane of the roof, with 48.3 × 4mm c.h.s. Glazing purlins of the same section run in the line

13

4.2.
(a) Plan. 1 Main entrance; 2
vehicular entrance; 3 forum; 4
internal street; 5 sheltered flats; 6
bedsits with communal lounge; 7
car parking; 8 gardens. (b)
Section. 1 Gardens; 2 bedsit; 3
communal lounge; 4 internal
street; 5 sheltered flat; 6 car
parking

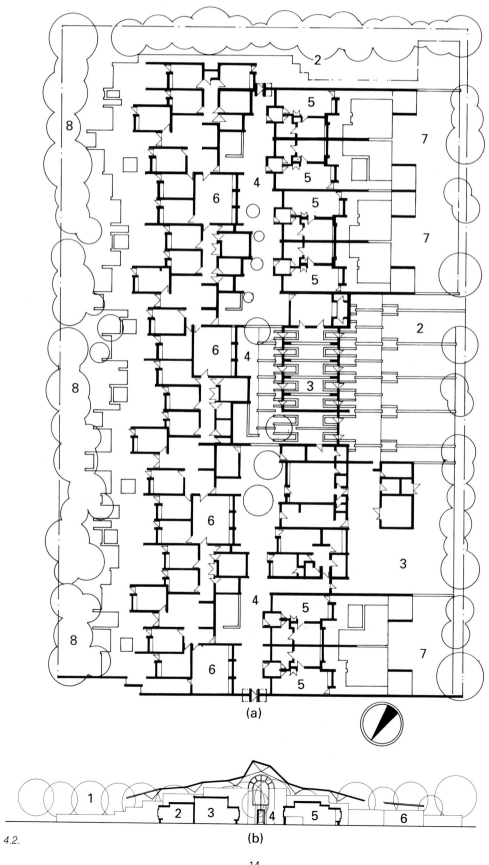

(a)

4.2.   (b)

4.4.
Trelliswork echoed in furniture design in communal 'forum'

4.5.
Internal street showing 'umbrella roof'

4.3.
Roof gutter and gargoyle discharging into pond. Note PVC skirt on underside of outer truss

4.3.

4.4.

4.5.

4.6.
Exploded view of roof arrangement. 1 PeVe Clair TKP 150/45 × 2.5 mm thick sheeting; 2 GRP flashing; 3 60 × 5 mm continuous mild steel flats; 4 roof trusses; 5 48.3 × 4 mm c.h.s. bracing members; 6 mild steel bracket; 7 concrete padstone; 8 glassfibre gutter unit with 'gargoyle'; 9 brickwork support wall

4.7.
Detail of roof fixing. 1 PeVe Clair TKP 150/45 × 2.5 mm thick sheeting; 2 GRP flashing; 3 Fakband V self-adhesive tape; 4 Sela 35 washer head drill screw (flashing and sheeting to have 15 mm diameter holes predrilled); 5 60 × 5 mm continuous mild steel flat; 6 65 mm long × 5 mm mild steel cleats at 600 mm centres; 7 5 mm thick gusset at 600 mm centres; 8 48.3 × 4 mm c.h.s.

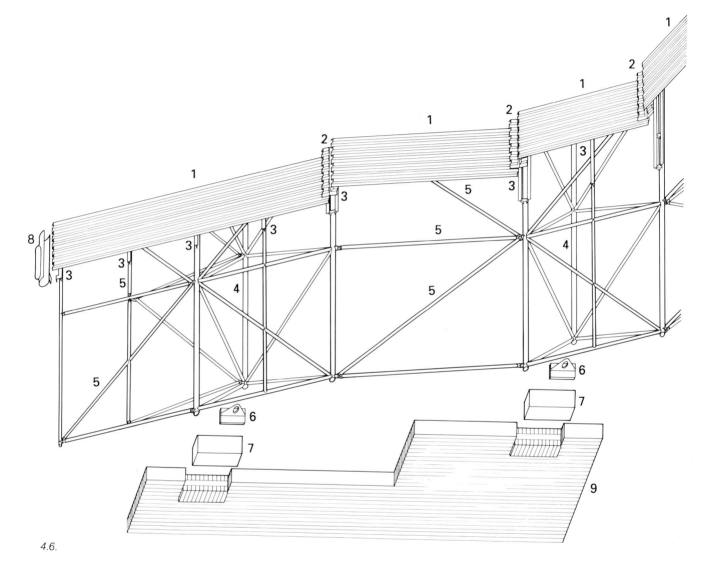

4.6.

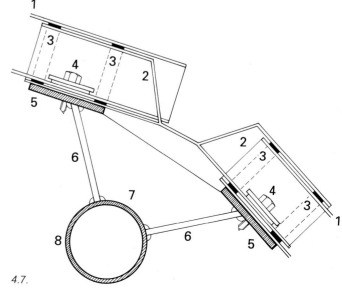

4.7.

of the trusses, the entire roof covering an area of 33.6 × 75.0 m (Figure 4.5). The roof finishes used are PeVe Clair clear (Isobelic) glazing (TKP 150/45 × 2.5 mm) and Plannja Profile Sheet roofing (45 × 0.55 mm) with PVF^2 finish. The sheet roofing is used over the flat-roof areas of the accommodation except where clerestory lighting is required.

The sheeting spans between trusses, and is supported on and connected to continuous 'flats' of mild steel (60 × 5 mm) welded to 5 mm cleats which are in turn welded to the top chord of the truss at 600 mm centres (Figure 4.6). The cleats are made rigid by means of 5 mm mild steel gussets welded between them at 600 mm centres.

A seal is made between two spans of roof finish by means of glass-reinforced polyester flashings, which are formed in the same profile as the sheeting. The flashing fits *below* the upper sheet and *above* the lower one, except at the apex of the central ridge, where it fits over both. Two strips of Fakband V tape (compressed size 10 × 3 mm) are used to seal each sheeting-to-flashing joint.

The PeVe Clair glazing and Plannja Profile sheet roofing are screwed to the mild steel support flats using Sela washer head drill screws (35 mm and 20 mm, respectively), allowing for expansion of 2.5 mm. The PeVe Clair glazing lengths have widths of 1200 mm, and the side laps are pop-riveted at 600 mm centres, also using a sealing strip. The Plannja sheet roofing has sealed rivets at 300 mm centres along the side laps. The GRP flashing is manufactured in widths corresponding with the PeVe Clair sheeting, plus 150 mm laps.

A PeVe Clair TKP 150/45 × 2.5 mm thick skirt is attached by means of flats (53 × 5 mm m.s.) welded to cleats (5 mm thick m.s. at 600 mm centres) to the underside of each of the two outermost trusses. These prevent rain from entering, but are not sealed and, together with the open-ended gables, allow air movement and are intended to reduce the possibility of heat gain under the 'umbrella'. A series of air vents are also provided in the roof plane above the uppermost truss (Figure 4.3).

Rainwater from the roof is collected in glassfibre gutter units, bolted to brackets welded at 1200 mm centres to the outer mild steel 'flats' which support the roof sheeting. Lengths of guttering are connected by means of a 50 mm spigot and socket joint, with seal-bolted connection. Instead of downpipes, the gutter is formed into 'gargoyles', each 600 mm wide, which discharge into ponds in the gardens below them.

References

Darley, G., 'Hampshire symbol', *Architectural Review*, **179**, No. 1072, June 1986, pp. 58–61.
Stansfield Smith, C., 'Public tribute', *Architects' Journal*, **183**, No. 5, 29 January 1986, pp. 20–23.

5.1.

Clarke Ascot House, Brisbane
Architect/owner
Chris Clarke

General

Built in 1985 on a steep hillside in the suburb of Ascot overlooking Brisbane, Australia, this unashamedly modern and finely detailed house is supported on a pristine white-painted r.h.s. steel frame sprung from just four foundation pads and is linked to a timber deck, surrounding a swimming pool, by two bridges (Figure 5.2). Owner/architect Chris Clarke designed the building with Mark Whitby (structural engineer) while nearing the end of a 15-year stay in England, having worked for John Winter for 10 years (he was involved in Winter's own Highgate House) and for Foster Associates, on the Hongkong and Shanghai Bank.

Clearly, Clarke has been influenced by Craig Elwood and Mies van der Rohe's ideas, and the house was conceived as a series of prefabricated elements which could be brought to site and bolted together as quickly as possible, thus eliminating the need for extensive work on a site virtually inaccessible to heavy machinery because of its slope (Figure 5.1). The low site costs offset the relatively high building costs, the result being an elegant re-interpretation of the local terrace lifestyle, suited to the subtropical climate, with house, terrace and pool interacting (Figure 5.3). Sliding glazed panels, aluminium louvres and strut-supported canopies finely

5.2.

control the environment, with water heated by a roof-mounted solar collector, but an air-conditioning unit is still required.

The Clarke house won an honourable mention in the 1986 Royal Australian Institute of Architects awards and represents a very high standard in component building design as an example to architects throughout the world.

5.3.

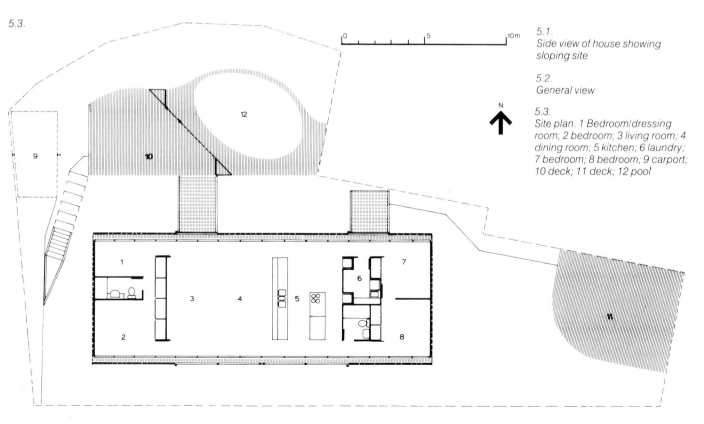

5.1.
Side view of house showing sloping site

5.2.
General view

5.3.
Site plan. 1 Bedroom/dressing room; 2 bedroom; 3 living room; 4 dining room; 5 kitchen; 6 laundry; 7 bedroom; 8 bedroom; 9 carport; 10 deck; 11 deck; 12 pool

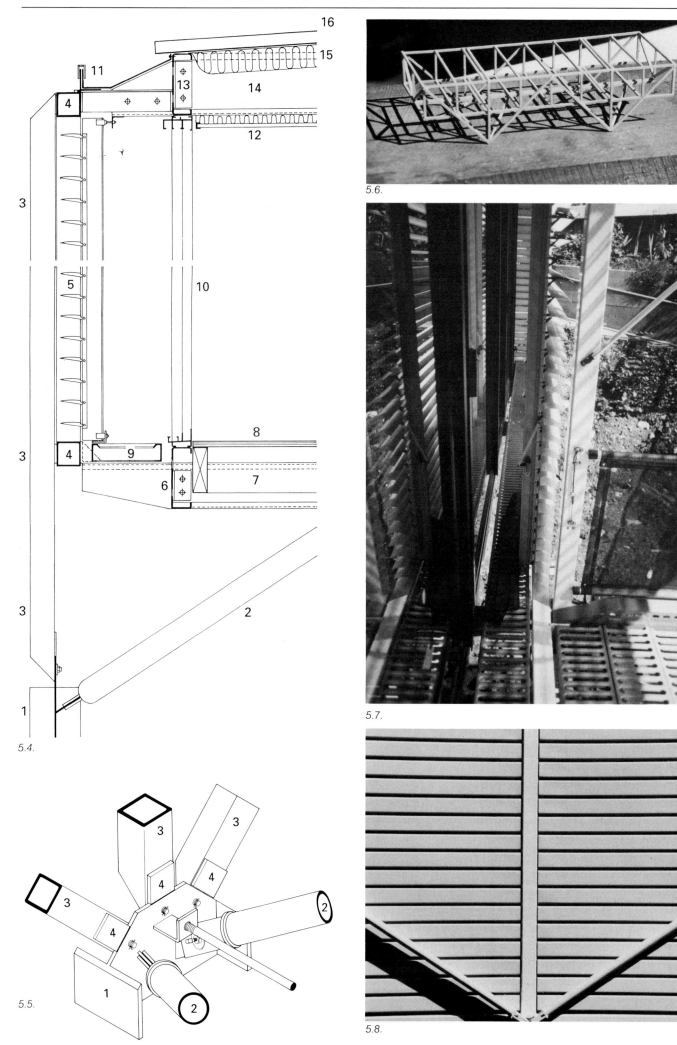

5.4.

5.5.

5.6.

5.7.

5.8.

*Construction details. 1 356 ×
171 mm mild steel stanchion; 2
80 mm diameter mild steel c.h.s.;
3. 80 × 80 mm r.h.s.; 4 80 ×
80 mm mild steel r.h.s. forming
frame structure; 5 adjustable
aluminium louvres; 6 perforated
steel channel forms edge beam; 7
150 × 50 mm hardwood joists at
450 mm centres; 8 20 mm tongue
and groove silver ash
floorboards; 9 walkway formed
from steel grating units; 10 sliding*

*anodized aluminium patio doors;
11 gutter support formed by 76 ×
76 × 5 mm mild steel angle with
continuous fillet weld to steel
frame; 12 perforated aluminium
ceiling strips with 25 mm acoustic
lining; 13 perforated steel channel
forms fascia; 14 pressed steel
roof beams; 15 75 mm foil-backed
glassfibre insulation quilt; 16 roof
formed from interlocking colour
coated galvanized steel profiled
roof decking fixed to 125 ×
50 mm hardwood purlins*

*Support bracket. 1 356 × 171 mm
UB cut to provide support
bracket; 2 80 mm diameter c.h.s.;
3 80 × 80 mm r.h.s.; 4 bearing
plate welded to back of diagonal
member*

*Architect's own model shows
clear structural intent*

*Zone between louvres and
glazing with standard floor
grating as walkway*

End-wall cladding

Structure

The key to this building is the box structure on four triangulated legs, as shown on the architect's own model (Figure 5.6). The simple geometric relationship, with the legs springing from the top corners down to the foundation pads and back to the centre, where they meet, results in the elegant final structural solution. All the main framing is constructed in 80 × 80 mm r.h.s. mild steel. The raking struts are tubular (80 mm diameter) and the tertiary structure is made up from standard cold-rolled sections. Roof studs and floor joists are mainly formed of hardwood.

The complete structure is bolted to four concrete foundation pads (Figure 5.5), the extra height on the south side being made up by 356 × 171 mm mild steel I-beam stanchions.

In detail, the inherent jointing complications of the rolled steel sections was overcome by cutting the ends at 45 degrees, thus facilitating face fixing.

Sequence of assembly (Figure 5.4)

The simplicity of the design depended upon an accurate and predetermined sequence of assembly as follows:

1. Lay and level foundation pads.
2. Then prop four identical four-bay storey-height frames on the long north and south elevations.
3. Bolt each pair together, forming an eight-bay wall.
4. Insert two-bay east and west elevation wall frames.
5. Insert roof and floor structure, thus stabilizing the entire building.
6. Apply roof finish and gutter.
7. Insert timber floor joists and floor decking.
8. Fit louvred ceiling with acoustic pads.
9. Fit internal partitions.
10. Fix perimeter glazed sliding doors and walking grills.
11. Complete internal plasterwork of end walls and painting.

Cladding

The long walls are entirely glazed in fixed and sliding anodized aluminium patio doors which are set back by 300 mm from the structural frame. This also supports the aluminium louvres in front of the window with standard steel grating units, forming a walkway between them (Figure 5.7). Using the same standard grating units, Clarke created the main entrance bridge with canopy above, leading from the entrance deck on the north

(sunny) side to the main living area. This canopy, with its adjustable struts, can be lowered to secure the house in the event of severe hailstorms, prevalent in the area, like a medieval castle.

The end walls are formed using fixed profiled aluminium sections (a Luxalon type 84R, Figure 5.8) on stringer supports fixed to 6 mm Versilux insulation board on 64 × 34 mm Gyproc boxed steel studs with 12 mm plasterboard forming the internal linings.

The roof is covered by an interlocking Klip-Lok profiled steel deck supported on 125 × 50 mm purlins and cambered to purpose-made 300 mm wide pressed steel gutters on both the long elevations with 75 mm foil-backed insulation below.

Internal finishes

Internally, the suspended ceiling is formed using perforated Luxalon 84C with 25 mm acoustic pads. The floor finish is silver ash, gun nailed to the joists, and coated with an ultraviolet light-stabilized polyurethane clear finish.

Services

Hot water is supplied by a solar collector mounted on the roof comprising a 300-litre tank and two black nickel-coated collectors. Air conditioning has also been installed. All rain and waste water runs to a point in the centre of the house and drains to the ground via a purpose-designed hopper and pipes attached to either side of an electrical ladder rack.

Costs

The high building costs ($600 per square metre) were offset by the inexpensive site and the small amount of foundation work necessary. Also, the steel frame was less susceptible to fungal and ant attack than the local timber buildings and thus has a longer life expectancy. Some similarities can be made between this building and the Yacht House by Richard Horden (Case Study 30), both architects perhaps influenced by their time at Foster Associates.

References

Brookes, A.J., 'A modern metal home', *Roof Cladding and Insulation*, July 1987, pp. 32–36.

Carolin, P., 'Brisbane bridge house', *Architects' Journal*, 6 August 1986, pp. 20–27.

6

Conservatory at Kew
Architects
Property Services Agency (Gordon Wilson)

General

Completed in 1986, this £4 million tropical conservatory was designed by the government's Property Services Agency for the Royal Botanic Gardens at Kew, south-west London (Figure 6.1). The design concept of a 'glazed hill' led to a stepped and staggered plan form, facing east–west, of five structural bays and clerestory-like gables glazed to let in a maximum amount of winter sunlight (Figures 6.2 and 6.3), covering 4490 m² (twice the area of the 1846 Palm House at Kew by Turner and Burton).

Portal-framed structure

The multi-span steel portal-framed structure is composed of a series of welded portal frames at 5.4 m centres. In some cases these frames span over five bays with props at each bay. Where the roof line changes, welded I-section mullions connect the top and bottom beams into the chords of a rectilinear lattice truss (Figure 6.4). The structure is braced against the wind by Vierendeel tubes (144 mm diameter) rigidly connected to the top flange of the I-beam forming the portal (Figure 6.5). In addition, these Vierendeel tubes also provide a secure anchorage for maintenance access. The roof pitch is 26.5 degrees, with the roof sloping down from the 11.4 m maximum ridge height to various ground levels externally.

6.1. General view

6.2.
Site plan. 1 Main gate; 2 Kew
Road entrance; 3 Princess of
Wales Conservatory; 4 Palm
House; 5 Temperate House

6.3.
Photograph of model showing
staggered plan form

6.4.
Lattice truss formed where roof
steps back

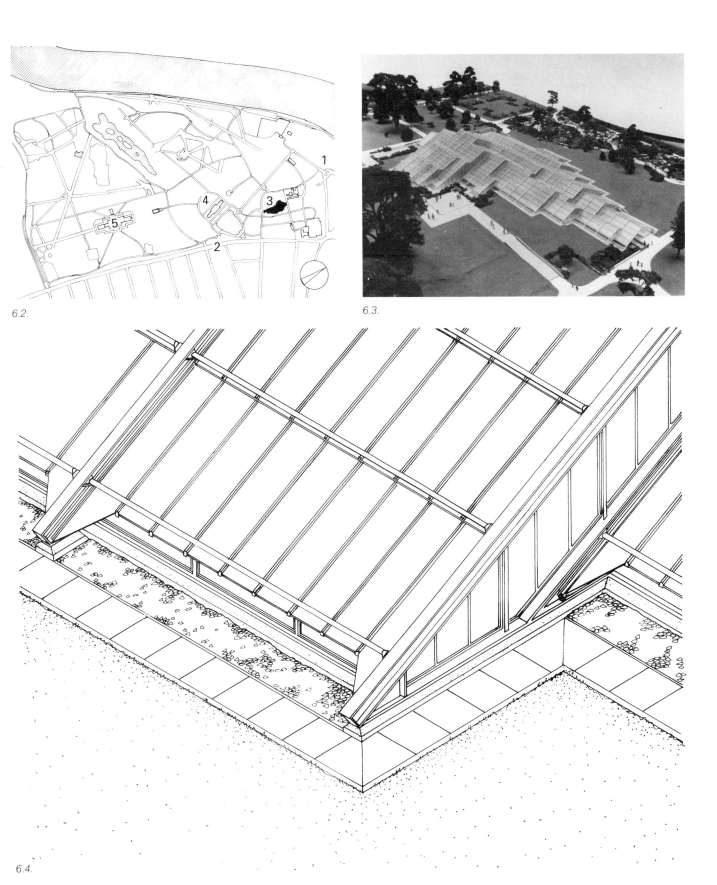

6.2.

6.3.

6.4.

6.5.
Detail showing connection of 114 mm diameter c.h.s. to top flange of portal

6.6.
Model showing valley gutter. Note purlins beside gutter to support glazing section

6.7.
Glazing lap detail. 1 Weather fillet with wiping seal and weephole to drain condensation; 2 6 mm rough-cast glass; 3 sliding fixing shoe for glazing bars; 4 glass stop; 5 compressed self-adhesive pad under stop to prevent blowback

6.8.
Section through glazing bar. 1 Pip on stem; 2 closed-cell EPDM; 3 extruded aluminium retaining wings; 4 rain-drainage channel; 5 condensation-drainage channel

Patent glazing

Early in the design process a decision had been taken to use patent glazing. The glazing subcontract for the conservatory was awarded to Pennycook Glazing (a wholly owned subsidiary of Ruberoid Contracts), who supplied and fixed the white powder-coated aluminium glazing bars glazed with 6 mm rough-cast glass.

Other glazing alternatives, including 6 mm float glass, 6 mm wired glass, double-glazed units and extruded multi-skin polycarbonate sheeting, had been considered. Eventually rough-cast glass with its rough face facing inwards was chosen to diffuse the sunlight, reduce the risk of scorching the plants and provide a diffuse background viewed from underneath, thus enhancing the tropical plants' form.

The patent glazing bar (Figure 6.8) was a modification of an existing section with a pip added to the stem of the extrusion to retain the glazing wings without the need for fixing clips. The most important innovation was the weather fillet provided for the sealed lap detail (Figure 6.7). This allows the patent glazing to lap but avoids algae collection associated with the normal method of overlapping the panes. The special fillet was designed to avoid draughts, to allow thermal movement between each glazing tier and, with the use of weepholes, to drain the condensation to the outside, thus avoiding the problem of dripping condensation on the plants below.

A continuous white polyester-coated extruded aluminium cap between the I-section of the portal frame and the glazing bars also serves to act as a cable duct which carries electrical services from a perimeter underground duct to environmental control equipment (Figure 6.9).

6.5.

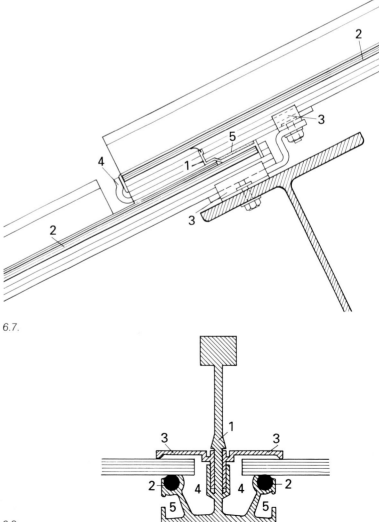

6.7.

6.6.

6.8.

6.9.
Section through rafter. 1 356 × 171 mm U-beam forming portal frame; 2 purlin; 3 continuous white polyester-coated extruded aluminium duct cap; 4 8 mm × 16 g white polyester-coated aluminium cover plate; 5 12 × 3 mm self-adhesive neoprene tape; 6 6 × 6 mm white silicone seal on 6 mm polythene cord; 7 extruded aluminium glazing bar; 8 6 mm rough-cast glass

6.10.
Zipper gasket at gables. (a) Glass to glass; (b) glass to steel section

6.11.
Valley gutter walkway hinged for access to gutter

Glazing to gable walls

Direct glazing to the steel mullions of the clerestory was achieved using neoprene gaskets supplied by Leyland and Birmingham Rubber Company. These zipper-type gaskets fit onto a 6 mm nib welded on the flanges of the primary I-beam and onto the machined-out flange of the H-sections (Figure 6.10). It is extremely difficult to control the accuracy of the steelwork necessary for such detail, and although a higher than standard degree of tolerance on the steelwork was achieved it was still necessary for the subcontractor to measure every opening on site and make up the gasket and glass size to suit.

Rainwater gutters

Water run off at the perimeter to soakaways and an internal valley gutter is placed between the two bottom purlins (Figures 6.6 and 6.11). A walkway is then arranged over the valley gutter with a chain-linked handrail bolted to the tubular wind bracing, which looks rather out of place compared to the rest of the detailing.

The building construction is worth further study, partly because of the straightforward hierarchy of the structural elements and partly because of the clever adaptation of patent glazing principles.

References

BSC Award, 'Princess of Wales Conservatory', *Steel Construction*, British Constructional Steelwork Association, November 1986.

Stacey, M., 'Construction study – glass – conservatory at Kew', *Architects' Journal*, 28 May 1986.

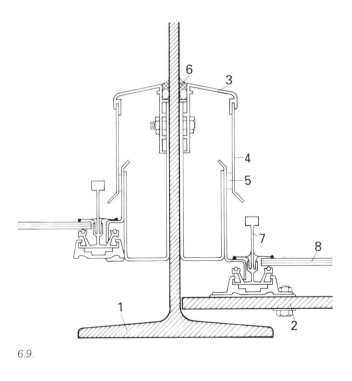

6.9.

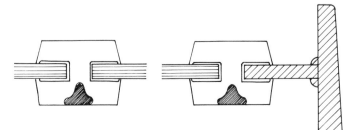

6.10.

6.11.

Cribbs Causeway Warehouses, Bristol
Architect
Building Design Partnership
Project architect
Gennaro Picardi

General

This development was built in 1986 for the Prudential Assurance Company, adjacent to junction 17 of the M5, at Bristol, and designed by BDP. It consists of two blocks of retail warehousing space providing 7000 and 9000 m² apiece (Figure 7.1). Built as empty shells for unspecified occupants, each structural bay can become a separate unit of approximately 1500 m² with individual service connections (Figure 7.2).

Structure

Both buildings are based upon a 3 m grid in both plan and section. Building A has a free-span structure of 21 × 21 m, and Building B a clear span of 18 × 12 m. The buildings are divided into bays by the main structural framework:

Building A: six bays, 21 m apart;
Building B: four bays, 21 m apart.

A secondary arched beam spans across each bay at 6 m centres. These, in turn, support the roof sheeting rails (Figure 7.3).

The gable walling is supported by vertical cladding rails of gable posts at 3 m intervals, with cross-bracing (Figure 7.4). This very straightforward sequence of structural parts is a model to a student attempting to understand a hierarchy of beam sizes for a rectangular structural form.

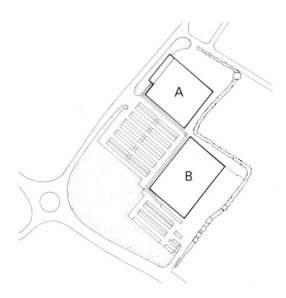

7.1.

Roofing

The roof shape takes the form of a shallow curve with a building height varying from 6 m at the gutter line to 8 m at the apex. The roof overhangs the front and rear elevations by 1 m, providing shading and weather protection (see Figures 7.2 and 7.4). Its construction is twin-skinned steel sheeting with site-assembled insulation (Figure 7.6). The roof profile used is the 'Architectural Profiles' (AP 22) for the external and internal metal roof sheets, separated and supported by zed spacer bars and the thermal break provided by a plastic spacer ferrule. Insulation is obtained by using 60 mm Rockwool insulation at 23 kg/m² density (to provide a U-value of 0.6 W/m²/°C) (Figure 7.5).

Wall sheeting

The wall-cladding construction on the side walls is similar to the roof specification with both internal and external sheeting using Architectural Profiles AP 22 profile. Sheeting is coated with PVF² Kynar 500, which consists of a primer coat, two coats of PVF² and a clear final coat with a total thickness of 50 microns. The colour is a special pale yellow. The profiled walls and roof were carried out by Hermcrest Southern Ltd, for Sir Robert McAlpine Ltd (main contractor).

Curtain walling on the end gables

There are two types of curtain walling on the building. Hermcrest provided the Slimwall system of curtain walling on the side walls. The gable facades are an interchangeable system of glazing and aluminium panels by Hans Schmidlin AG. These glazed panels are double-glazed in toughened glass, 6 mm thick anti-sun green externally and 6 mm clear float toughened internally to the bottom-glazed units. The remaining units, with a reduced requirement for impact resistance, have 6 mm clear float internally.

The pressed aluminium panels, downpipe and hoppers are coated in Colorsec powder coating, colour metallic silver to the external sheeting, off-white to the internal sheeting and bright yellow for the downpipes and hoppers.

As with all curtain wall systems, adjustment is required to allow for inaccuracy of the adjacent construction. In this case it is provided by the cast aluminium spacer bracket specially made by Schmidlin for this project. This translates the tolerances of the gable posts and allows alignment of the vertical sheeting rails (Figure 7.7).

7.1.
Site plan

7.2.
Rear elevation of bays

7.3.
Arched beams at 6 m centres with sheeting rails

7.4.
Gable wall prior to cladding

7.2.

7.3.

7.4.

7.5.
Construction details

7.6.
View of roof at eaves shows twin
skins of profiled steel sheeting
with site-assembled insulation

7.7.
Foot of gable post with cast
aluminium curtain walling support
bracket and curtain walling
mullion

7.5.

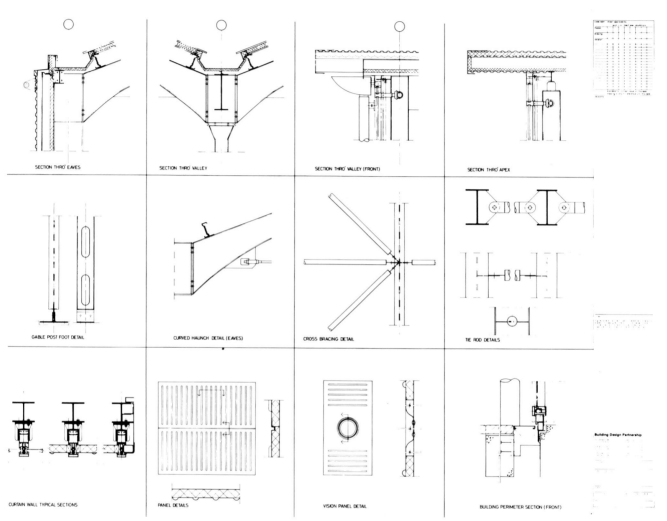

SECTION THRO' EAVES

SECTION THRO' VALLEY

SECTION THRO' VALLEY (FRONT)

SECTION THRO' APEX

GABLE POST FOOT DETAIL

CURVED HAUNCH DETAIL (EAVES)

CROSS BRACING DETAIL

TIE ROD DETAILS

CURTAIN WALL TYPICAL SECTIONS

PANEL DETAILS

VISION PANEL DETAIL

BUILDING PERIMETER SECTION (FRONT)

Building Design Partnership

7.6.

7.7.

7.8.
Details of hopper head

7.9.
Covered walkway

7.10.
Escape door and ladder rail

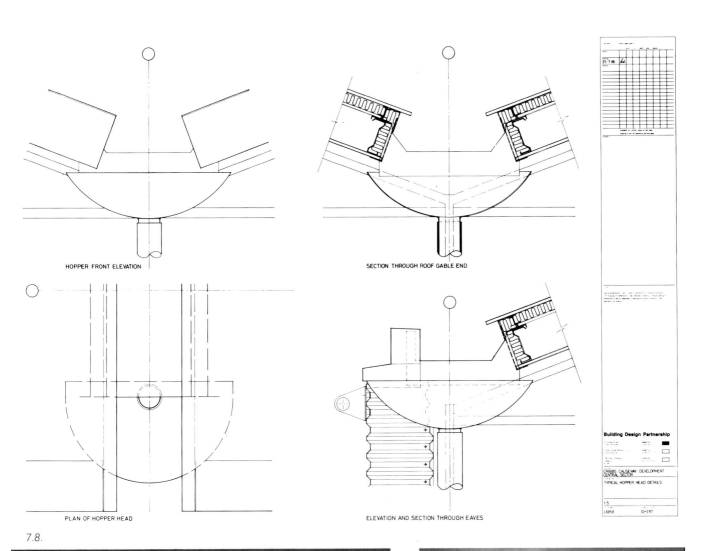

HOPPER FRONT ELEVATION

SECTION THROUGH ROOF GABLE END

PLAN OF HOPPER HEAD

ELEVATION AND SECTION THROUGH EAVES

Building Design Partnership

CRIBBS CAUSEWAY DEVELOPMENT
CENTRAL SECTOR

TYPICAL HOPPER HEAD DETAILS

1:5

L6858   (0–)97

7.8.

7.9.

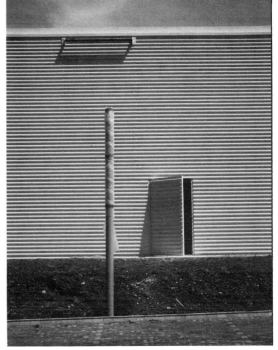

7.10.

Covered walkway

A continuous 3 m wide tubular steel covered walkway provides both a visual and physically protective link for customers to the front elevation of both retail warehousing blocks. The covering is formed by a green translucent polycarbonate dome with the detail of the column head with its four projecting flanges providing not only support to the beams but also a means of allowing tenant signage. It also allows further extension of lightweight structure to the walkway canopy (Figure 7.9).

Accessories

An interesting feature of this building is the careful choice of hopper fronts and gutters, as detailed by BDP (Figure 7.8). These add a refinement to the overall appearance. Similarly, fire doors have been carefully detailed to match the profile of the cladding. Also, ladder support rails have been provided in various positions in 75 mm diameter aluminium with plastic protection to allow roof access without damaging the edge guttering (Figure 7.8). The high quality of detailing for an industrial building of this type is illustrated by the concern for junction conditions between components and quality control over such items as thickness of sheeting carried out by the architect.

There are some interesting parallels that can be drawn between this approach to detailing and that by the Australian architect Glen Murcutt in his Kempsey Museum (Case Study 17).

References

Brookes, A.J. and Stacey, M., 'Fast facades', *Building Products*, December 1987, pp. 81–91.

Copeland, S., 'Development economics', *Architects' Journal*, 18 February 1987, pp. 61–66.

The Customs House, Hazeldonk
Architects
Benthem and Crouwel

General

This prototype for a number of customs houses is situated in Hazeldonk, near Breda in the south of Holland, close to the Belgian border, and was built in 1984 (Figure 8.1). It consists of a rectangular plan of raised offices below a space-frame roof with two storeys of smaller offices and ancillary rooms separated from the main space by a glazed corridor (Figure 8.2). The offices look out over a carpark which contains a further space-frame structure used for customs inspection of containers (Figure 8.3).

Structure

The space-frame structure (seven bays wide by 38 bays long, each bay 1800 mm) is held on two pairs of seven V-shaped legs at 10.8 m centres, thus forming a series of squares each seven bays × 1.8 m on their lower booms and eight bays × 1.8 m on their top ones. This could be seen to be an ideal arrangement for a space-frame construction of approximately 1.8 m in depth.

The connection between the space frames made by Octatube (Delft) uses an unusual method of bolting the flattened ends of the tubular steel chords onto a specially welded plate (Figure 8.4), thus avoiding the expensive node connection normally associated with space decks. (This system was used in Benthem and Crouwel's house in Almere: see Case Study 2.) The legs of the structure

8.1.

8.1.
General view

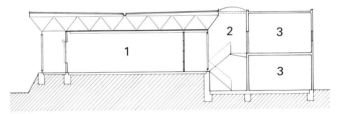

8.2.
8.2.
Section through Customs House.
1 Customs hall; 2 glazed corridor;
3 offices

8.3.
Inspection shelter with Customs
House in the background

8.3.

8.4.
Space-frame nodes and V-shaped support legs

8.5.
Welded steel base bracket

8.6.
Section through curtain walling

are bolted at their base to welded steel brackets bolted to the concrete block (Figure 8.5).

Cladding

The cladding to the main office areas is constructed using the Astrawall system and assembled by J. Hermans of Tienen. The overall assembly of 4 no. solid or glazed panels each 745 mm high is connected back to an aluminium carrier system with a box section approximately 120 mm and 50 mm (Figure 8.6). The two centre bands consist of double-glazed units, one of which is openable, and the top and bottom solid panels are made using a sandwich panel of 6 mm glass, 50 mm polyurethane and 1.5 mm aluminium inner skin (Figure 8.7). The corners of the curtain wall assembly are formed by a solid L-shaped panel mounted into the curtain wall section and painted black to match (Figure 8.8). Cill detail to the upstand concrete slab includes an aluminium strip fascia mounted into the carrier transom (Figure 8.9).

Roof

Strangely, the building has a double roof layer with the outer skin comprising a single-skin profiled steel roof deck and the inner one supported by purlins which are hung from the bottom booms of the space deck. These form the thermal and acoustic barrier as a continual box around the office areas. The edges of the roof deck support the curtain wall framing by means of a 120 × 80 × 10 mm roof-edge member (Figure 8.10).

The roof of the container shelter is a metal deck suspended from purlins fixed to the bottom booms, thus inverting the upper roof structure of the office block accommodation. The classic problem of roof drainage from an overhanging roof has been dealt with in this case by the somewhat uncomfortable detail using downpipes following the shape of the structural props. Large deflections can also be expected in a roof of this type.

Services

Services to the customs house are provided by ducts mounted within the depth of the space frame, between the two roofs. External blinds are mounted on the curtain walling assembly above the opening windows.

References

Berni, L. and Leroy, A., 'Holland: a constructive workshop', *Ottagono*, March 1987, pp. 20–33.

Buchannan, P., 'High tech and high style', *Architectural Review*, January 1985, pp. 56–59.

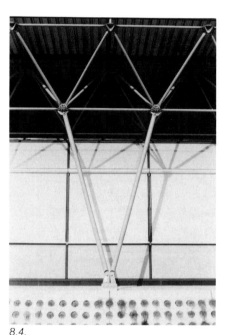

8.4.

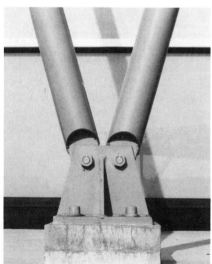

8.5.

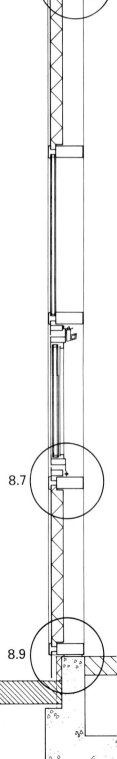

8.10

8.7

8.9

8.6.

8.7.
Section through cladding transom. 1 50 × 115 mm extruded aluminium transom section; 2 sandwich panel: 6 mm glass, 50 mm polyurethane insulation, 1.5 mm aluminium inner skin; 3 gasketed cover strip; 4 opening glazed panel

8.8.
Plan of corner detail. 1 50 × 115 mm extruded aluminium mullion sections; 2 L-shaped corner panel; 3 30 × 30 × 2 mm aluminium angle; 4 fixed glazed panel; 5 opening glazed panel; 6 gasketed cover strip

8.9.
Detail at base. 1 50 × 115 mm extruded aluminium transom; 2 5 mm thick aluminium strip; 3 35 mm thick 'foamglass' insulation; 4 sandwich panel: 6 mm glass, 50 mm polyurethane insulation, 1.5 mm aluminium inner skin; 5 gasketed cover strip; 6 concrete perimeter edge beam

8.10.
Detail at roof. 1 120 × 80 × 10 mm roof-edge member suspended off bottom of space frame; 2 50 × 115 mm extruded aluminium transom section bolted to roof-edge member; 3 gasketed cover strip; 4 aluminium coping; 5 profiled aluminium decking with 60 mm polyurethane insulation; 6 single-skin membrane roof covering

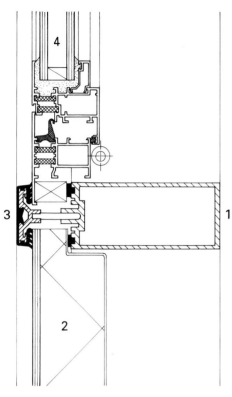

8.7.

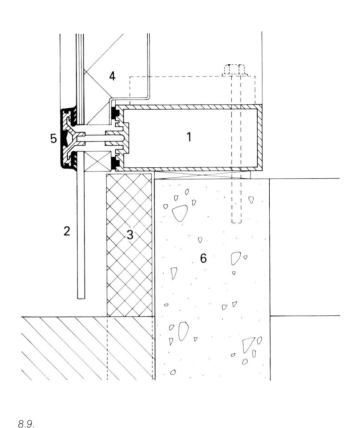

8.9.

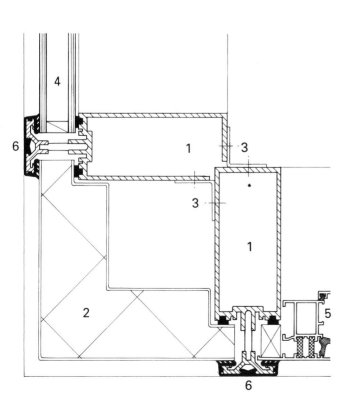

8.8.

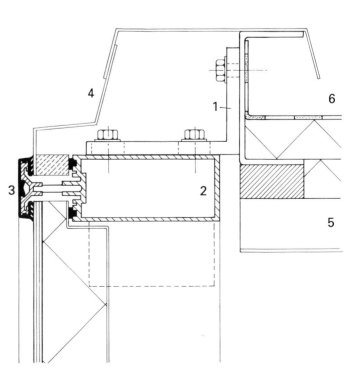

8.10.

33

Darling Harbour Exhibition Centre
Architects
Philip Cox and Partners

General

This building, with its tall-masted structure, is situated near the Chinese area of Sydney, Australia, and is part of the dockland redevelopment of Sydney's Darling Harbour. The site is bisected by a series of elevated motorways from which the roof of the building can be seen (Figure 9.1). This creates an unusual requirement for the building, whose construction can be observed from all levels. The plan shape is a series of five staggered bays following the line of the freeway overhead (Figure 9.4), each bay being independently structured by four supporting masts, forming the large exhibition centre with a height to the underside of the main beams of 13.5 m.

The project was a mangement contract by Leighton Contractors Pty Ltd, using architects Philip Cox and Partners and engineers Ove Arup and Partners.

Structure

A typical structural bay is shown in Figure 9.3, and consists of four masts, each being a group of four c.h.s. steel columns arranged in a square and bolted at their base to the concrete slab (Figure 9.5). From these masts four sets of triangular trusses spanning 15 m are supported by rods at their ends. These are pinned at their ends to allow movement using stainless steel pins (Figure 9.6).

From the ends of these trusses and from the masts span four main beams pinned at their centre, spanning a total of 92 m, with rods from the masts supporting these beams along their length (Figure 9.7) and with a triangular cross-section lattice outrigger 13.5 m long, also suspended at its ends by rods from the masts. The method of separating out these rod connections at the head of the mast to avoid complicated junctions is of interest (Figure 9.8), and this should be compared with Victoria Plaza (Case Study 31). The ends of the rods have cast fork connectors through which pass the steel pins into the welded plates on the beams and columns.

Comparison can also be made with Stansted Airport (see case Study 27). Both structures have four columns per mast which are bolted down to the concrete base. Stansted has 4 no. 457 mm c.h.s. at 3 m centres supporting a structure which spans 36 m in both directions. Darling Harbour has 4 no. 406 mm c.h.s. at approximately 1 m centres supporting a structure which spans a total of 92 m in one direction and 26.3 m in the other, using cable supports. Between the main beams the roof beams spanning 26.3 m are curved to allow a roof slope. These then support curved purlins taking the

9.1.

9.2.

roof sheeting (Figure 9.2).

It is this hierarchy of structural members that should interest students of component assembly. However, it is likely that the weight of steel is more than normally expected for a structure of these spans. The result, with its white-painted steelwork against a bright blue Australian sky, is a very graceful and elegant design solution.

Cladding

Cladding panels consisting of 35 mm steel faced sandwich panels by H.H. Robertson, 900 mm in height, span onto vertical cladding rails bolted to a secondary frame (Figure 9.9) and are surrounded at their edges by glazed strips between the roof and at the main mast positions. These panels are finished with an embossed epoxy coating in two colours to produce a striped effect. The glazed strips between the panels are formed using conventional curtain wall framing fixed back onto the cladding supports (Figure 9.10). The composite panels

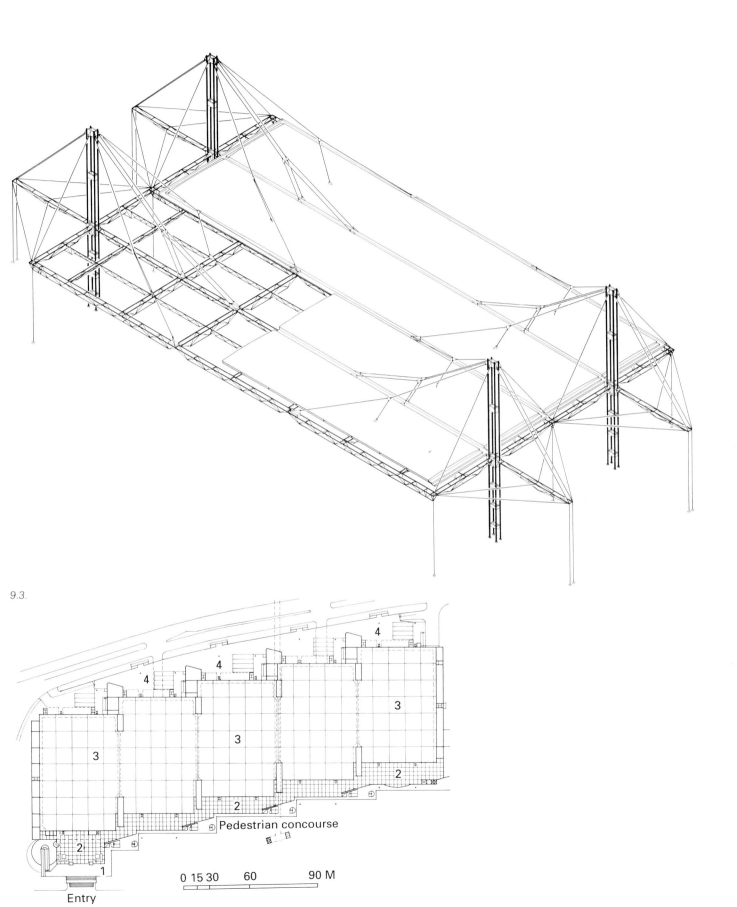

9.1.
View of roof from motorway

9.2.
Curved purlins

9.3.
General arrangement of one structural bay

9.4.
Site plan. 1 Entrance; 2 foyer; 3 main halls; 4 loading bays

9.3.

9.4.

Pedestrian concourse

4

4

4

3

3

3

2

2

2

1

Entry

0 15 30   60   90 M

9.5.
Columns fixed to concrete foundations by anchor bolts. 1 406 mm c.h.s. mast members; 2 box girder connecting mast members; 3 anchor bolts to foundations

9.6.
Junction between masts and trusses. 1 406 mm c.h.s. mast member; 2 273 mm c.h.s. top chord of primary truss; 3 10 mm mild steel plate; 4 168 mm c.h.s. top chord of perimeter truss

9.7.
Rod supports to trusses. 1 60 mm diameter steel rods; 2 168 mm c.h.s. top chord of secondary truss; 3 273 mm c.h.s. top chord of primary truss

9.8.
Junction between mast head and rods. 1 90 mm diameter steel rod; 2 50 mm diameter steel rod; 3 60 mm diameter steel rod; 4 406 mm c.h.s. mast member; 5 850 × 180 mm box girder connecting mast members

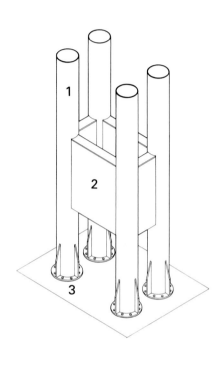

9.5.

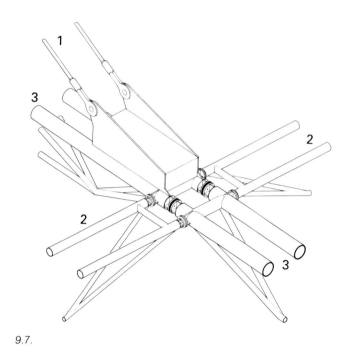

9.7.

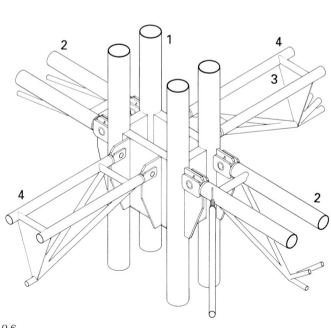

9.6.

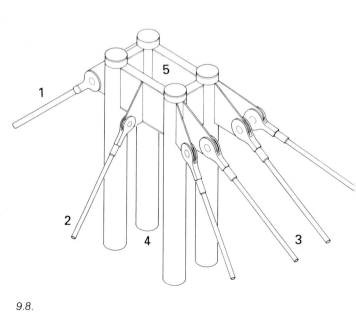

9.8.

9.9.
Sectional perspective through typical wall. 1 Ribbed steel roof deck; 2 rainwater gutter; 3 primary truss, 1200 mm deep; 4 vertical wall truss; 5 insulated sandwich panel; 6 30 mm diameter steel anchor rod; 7 canopy over loading bay; 8 4 × 406 mm c.h.s. mast; 9 20 mm diameter steel cable; 10 90 mm diameter steel rods; 11 outrigger truss; 12 75 mm diameter anchor rods; 13 glazed zone

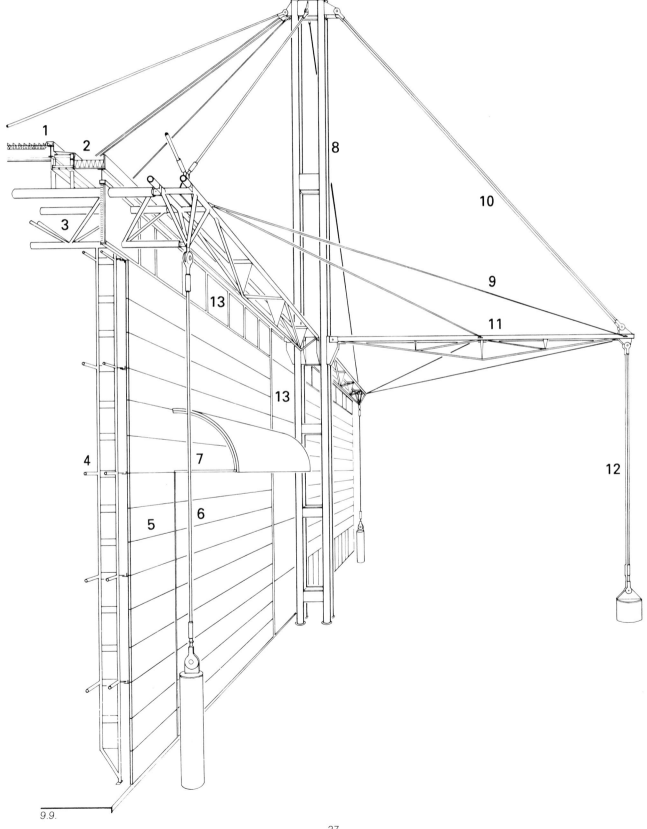

9.9.

9.10.
Curtain wall with glazed zone

9.11.
Cladding fixed back to blockwork

9.12.
*Cladding cleats. (a) Factory
welded. (b) Site welded*

9.10.

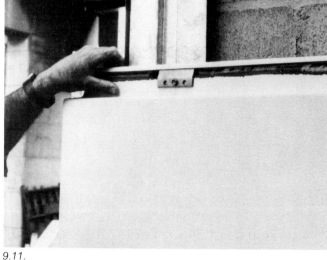

9.11.

9.12a.

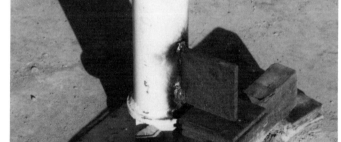

9.12b.

are also fixed back to solid walls in some positions, using aluminium cleats bolted through to a galvanized top-hat section, fixed to the blockwork (Figure 9.11). Corner panels are formed by cutting the back skin of the panel and re-sealing with a silicone joint.

An interesting site problem of fixing the cladding rails to their cleats resulted in these having to be re-welded and site drilled to take up deviations in alignment (Figure 9.12b). The problem of tolerances in component assembly cannot be overemphasized, and any means of taking up three-dimensional variations, particularly in the main

structure, should be employed (i.e. using slotted connections). (See also Case Study 32 for curtain wall fixing to the Hongkong and Shanghai Bank.)

References

Ogg, A., *Architecture in Steel, the Australian Context*, RAIA, 1987, pp. 191–198.

Quarry, N., 'Darling development', *Architectural Review*, February 1987, pp. 70–73.

10

The Devonshire Building, Boston, Mass.
Architects
Steffian and Bradley Associates

General

Situated in Devonshire Street, Boston, Massachusetts, USA, near the Boston City Hall, this mixed-use high-rise structure was built in 1983 as a speculative development of offices, apartments and a top-floor health club with swimming pool and underground parking for 220 cars. This building represents a faction of current architectural design leaning towards sleek, smooth, flat facades using aluminium as a curtain wall skin in front of a more traditional construction to achieve the performance requirements for thermal, fire and acoustics (Figure 10.1). As such, although it cannot be considered particularly significant in the context of world architecture, it may be interesting for the student of construction to note the relatively low-cost nature of the curtain walling assembly now described.

Construction of external wall

The entire exterior surface of the building is clad with Fluoropolymer-coated aluminium Alucobond panels, consisting of two sheets of aluminium (Peralumen NS41) each 0.5 mm thick, bonded to a low-density polyethylene core. These panels, formed to shape, are combined with anodized aluminium windows (Figure 10.2).

Detail

At each of the 40 floor levels a 100 × 38 mm continuous steel channel section is fixed by adjustable brackets back to the floor slab. To this is mounted the extruded aluminium carrier system for the windows and Alucobond panels formed into a tray, which is also fixed into the same section. These aluminium panels are formed by cutting the inner skin of the Alucobond and the core and allowing the outer 25 mm of aluminium skin to bend inwards at a 90-degree angle. Extruded aluminium stiffeners running lengthwise were attached to the back of the panels using silicone cement. The stiffeners also support the panel by resting on adjustable clips fixed back to the continuous steel channel.

Opening and fixed double-glazed window sections are also attached to the carrier system and the whole assembly is face sealed using Silpruf sealant on a Denver foam backing strip (Figure 10.3). The visual expression of both the vertical and horizontal joints is then created using these 63 mm wide × 3 mm aluminium plates, face fixed through into the carrier system with a

10.1.

1.5 × 18 mm neoprene isolator cemented to the mullions and transoms to form a thermal break.

Clearly, the main problem with this kind of face-fixed plate is the butt-joint junction between the plates and the face-fix screws and washers (Figure 10.4). Accuracy in the cutting of the ends of the plates and the method of sealing between them would be extremely significant in a building where this detail could be immediately noticed at eye level. On a 40-storey building in a busy city street, such as the Devonshire Building, this may not be quite as significant. At the back of the assembly, metal stud and dry wall lining is used with insulation provided by fibreglass bats.

10.1.
General view down Devonshire
Street

10.2.
Detail of opaque panel and
opening double-glazed window.
1 125 × 75 mm steel angle
anchored to concrete slab; 2 100
× 38 mm continuous steel
channel; 3 extruded aluminium
carrier system; 4 Alucobond tray;
5 aluminium stiffener; 6
adjustable clip; 7 opening

double-glazed unit; 8 Silpruf
sealant with Denier backing foam;
9 63 × 3 mm aluminium cover
plate fixed back with stainless
steel screw on neoprene washer

10.3.
Single- and double-glazed
windows. 1 Extruded aluminium
carrier system; 2 fixed double-
glazed panel; 3 fixed single-
glazed panel; 4 63 × 3 mm
aluminium cover plate fixed back
with stainless steel screw on
neoprene washer

10.4.
Isometric of cladding assembly. 1
Concrete floor slab; 2 125 ×
75 mm steel angle; 3 100 ×
38 mm continuous steel channel;
4 extruded aluminium carrier
system; 5 Alucobond tray; 6 63 ×
3 mm aluminium cover plate fixed
back with stainless steel screw on
neoprene washer; 7 double-
glazed unit

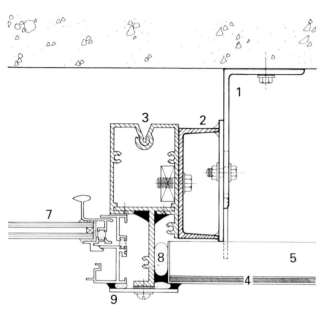

10.2.

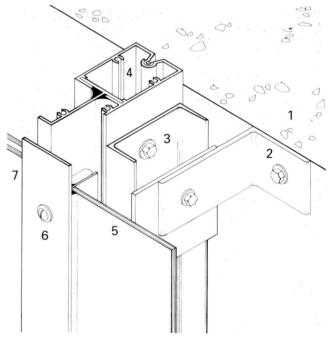

10.4.

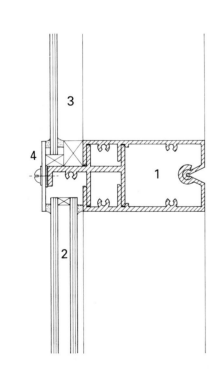

10.3.

11

1 Finsbury Avenue, London (Phase 1)
Architects/Engineers/Quantity Surveyors
Arup Associates

General

One Finsbury Avenue is part of a three-phase develop-ment built on land owned by British Rail (Figure 11.1). Greycoat Estates were the developers and Arup Associ-ates the architects, engineers and quantity surveyors.

Arup Associates designed an eight-storey atrium building which, by stepping back from the elevation at the sixth floor, maintains the existing urban scale (Figure 11.2). The architects have created a series of planted balconies at the upper levels on all but the south facade. The design of the facades incorporates a system of sunscreens and maintenance walkways which also create a human scale (Figure 11.3). Balconies, sun-shades, screens and planting add richness to the central atrium space which is enclosed by a glazed lantern (Figure 11.5).

This building, designed on a square grid, is beautifully detailed and represents a new approach in speculative office building, where the quality of the workplace is important as well as simple efficiently used space. Arup Associates have carefully detailed the interior to allow a great versatility in planning and subdivision. Ceiling tiles, light fittings and air inlets are all easily movable.

Structure

The developers' need for a rapid site erection, coupled with recent requirements for steel fireproofing, allowed spraying of fireproofing onto the steel as an alternative to complete encasement of steelwork in concrete. This led the architects to design a steel-framed structure with steel decking and concrete slab floors. The frame made up from a total of 1500 tons of steel, was in UB and UC sections, and in order to achieve maximum economy the design was based on a simple rectilinear form with repetitive elements and simple bolted connections. Horizontal stability is achieved by diagonally braced frames in the core area.

The floor slab is 130 mm deep overall, constructed on 1.1 mm profiled steel sheeting spanning 3 m and using a lightweight aggregate pumped concrete mix. The con-crete slab then acts compositely with the profiled steel sheeting as well as the frame beams by steel shear studs welded to the beams through the profile sheets.

The frame and slabs took 13 weeks to erect on site. The entire process from start on-site to completion of the building took 21 months at a cost of £20 million. External columns at ground-floor level were encased in concrete

Sun Street

Phase 2

Phase 3

Broadgate
Phase 1

Wilson Street

Phase 1

Finsbury Avenue

Broadgate
Phase 2

11.1.
Location plan

11.2.
East elevation showing stepped-back balconies on sixth floor, thus reducing the visual bulk of the building

11.1.

11.2.

11.3.
North–south section showing
central atrium with floors stepping
back

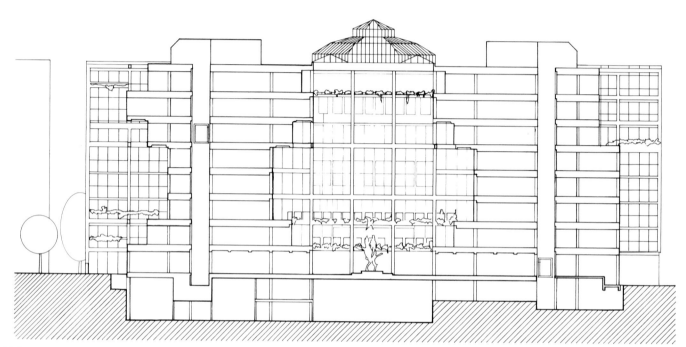

11.3.

and, wherever possible, this process was carried out at the fabrication works. Exposed columns within the building are faced in metal-faced fireboard for protection.

Cladding

The integrated curtain walling system by Joseph Gartner incorporates a patented system whereby hot water is circulated through the r.h.s. members forming the mullions and the transoms of the subframe to which the glazing carrier system is fixed. This provides the only heat source necessary in the building to counteract the main heat loss at the perimeter. The curtain walling is in bronze-anodized aluminium, with panels of the same material being used to clad the frame itself and the externally exposed stairwells. Bronze-coloured glass is used for the spandrel panels. At the ground floor, polished granite is used instead of the bronze-anodized aluminium as the cladding material, and the unpolished variety of the same stone is used as a paving material.

The external louvred sunscreens, which also act as maintenance walkways, are in bronze-anodized aluminium, with elegant edge beams and vertical supports in cruciform aluminium sections (Figure 11.4). Because of the uneven storey heights it has not been possible to maintain a square grid and thus the cross bracing is not lined through. The sunscreens provide shade on the east and west elevations, reducing the load on the air-conditioning system while providing visual interest to the street.

Details

Internally, the atrium opens out after first-storey height. All metalwork is aluminium finished in white synthapulvin, except for the grey-finished mullions and handrails, which employ the same aluminium extrusion as is used in the internal sunshade frames. The structural members of the octagonal glazed lantern also act as the glazing bars, rather than using separate systems. A swivelling gantry enables access to each surface to allow cleaning and maintenance. However, it is the layering and cruciform detail of the support to the external walkway which demonstrates the commitment by the design team to the use of modern materials to enhance the overall scale of the building.

As Peter Buchanan says: 'Arups have provided an object lesson for all architects. They prove that spec. offices can make a sensitive contribution to a civic environment, and that even a huge office building can have a richness and delicate scale suggestive of the human beings who work within – and who will no doubt be enjoying the building too.'

References

Anon., '1 Finsbury Avenue, London: Phase 1', *The Arup Journal*, pp. 2–7.
Buchanan, P., 'Urban Arups', *Architectural Review*, May 1985, pp. 21–30.
Davies, C., 'Craft or calculation', *Architectural Review*, May 1985, pp. 19–20.

11.4.

11.4.
Cruciform aluminium section

11.5.
Glazed lantern echoing Victorian
ironwork

11.5.

11.6.
*Section through integrated
curtain walling/heating system*

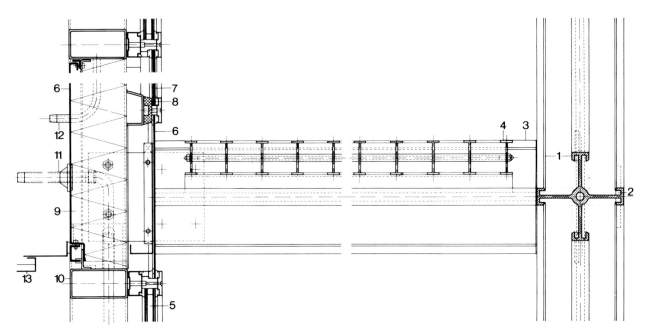

11.6

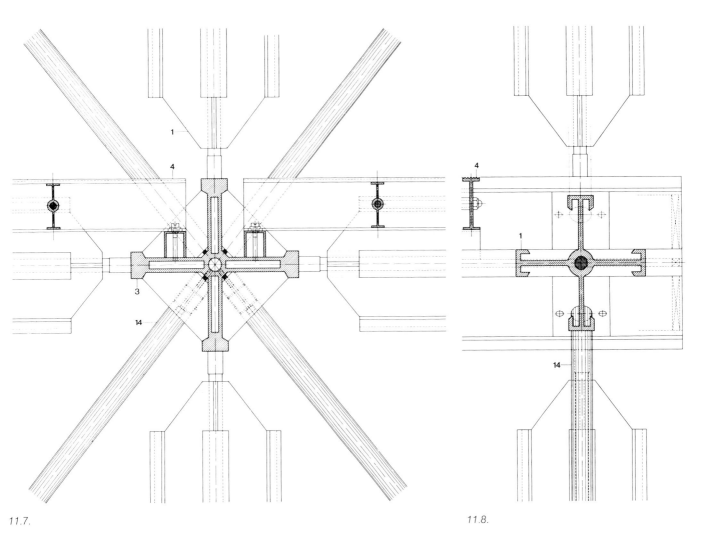

11.7.

11.8.

Details

1	Aluminium-shape 180/180 mm	6	Aluminium-cladding 3 mm
2	Angle 50/50 mm	7	Spandrel glazing
3	Aluminium-cantilever 230/230 mm	8	Gasket
4	Aluminium-grill, sun-blinds	9	Insulation
5	Double glazing	10	Steel section 120/60 mm, heated
		11	Return pipe for heating

12 Supply pipe for heating
13 Suspended ceiling
14 Diagonal bracing,
   stainless pipe Ø 30/5 mm
15 Cantilever fixing
   steel plate 340/180/12 mm

IBM Travelling Technology Exhibition
Architect
Renzo Piano

12.1.

General

This unique demountable structure was used as a travelling exhibition for IBM during 1984/1985 with sites as varied as Madrid and Helsinki. Under the supervision of Chris Wilkinson Architects, the pavilion was assembled at the Natural History Museum in London and at York (Figure 12.1). Two pavilions were fabricated and erected by the Sicilian firm of Calabrese Engineering SpA, to the original design of Renzo Piano and developed with the assistance of Ove Arup and Partners. Twenty-three specially designed bright-yellow trucks were used to transport the exhibition.

Structure

The structure is composed of 34 three-pinned arches (Figure 12.3) to a radius of 5.3 m with a single timber chord at 5.9 m radius joining the tops of the polycarbonate pyramids forming the skin. Each half arch comprises six polycarbonate pyramids, with three pyramids moulded out of a single sheet. The key cross section (Figure 12.2) shows how the polycarbonate acts as diagonal struts joining the timber chord members made of laminated beech with cast aluminium connectors. For transport, each arch was separated into four major components:

1. Two outer-chord timber members;
2. Four inner-chord timber members;

3. Fourteen inner-chord cross members;
4. Four sets of three pyramids.

The 600 mm deep half arch was then assembled on site by fixing the outer timber chords to the two sets of polycarbonate pyramids using stainless steel washers glued to two faces of the apex of the pyramid (Figure 12.4) (Dini, p. 78, shows Renzo Piano's original method of connecting the polycarbonate to its supporting framework which was later developed for the IBM travelling exhibition.) Figure 12.5 shows the formed stainless steel plate (a Kinch plate, named after Robert Kinch, one of the engineers working at Ove Arup and Partners) bolted to these washers with a rubber block cast on a rod radiating from the plate. This rubber block has a push fit into the external aluminium nodes connecting the outer timber chords. The pyramids are connected to the inner timber by 200 mm long stainless steel rods (Figure 12.6). A stainless steel block with a rotating cross pin is glued to the polycarbonate and the rod is screwed into the cross pin (Figure 12.7). The other end of the rod has a rubber block cast on and pushed into the aluminium node of the inner timber chords. At the base of the assembly the inner chords are pinned to a stainless steel plate (Figure 12.8) bolted to the edge beam. An important feature of this construction is that these movable metal rods allow for the differential thermal movement between the polycarbonate and that of the wood and aluminium struts.

Thus the construction is significant both in the way it

12.1.
The IBM pavilion at York

12.2.
Cross section through pavilion

12.3.
Plan of pavilion

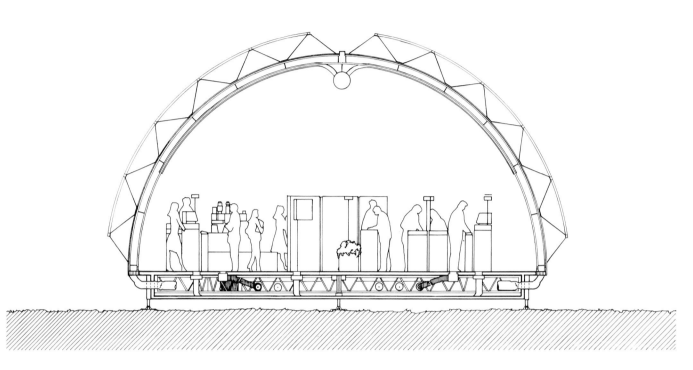

12.2.

overcomes the difference in thermal movement of the components used and the method of connecting the polycarbonate to the timber using the stainless steel connectors which made ease of assembly possible, even allowing for temperature and tolerance effects. Also of interest to the student of prefabrication is the elegant means of connecting the beechwood struts with the cast aluminium nodes (Figure 12.6), which shows how traditional craftsmanship of finger jointing can be translated into new material.

Polycarbonate panels

The polycarbonate pyramids were produced as a unit in sets of three, partly to ease transportation in relation to their length but also because 8.5 m was the maximum

length of sheet available for fabrication. These units were joined with an overlap detail at their horizontal joint. The vertical weather joint between the polycarbonate units was achieved by a thin transparent PVC strip fed down between the units which was disposable and replaced at each assembly (Figure 12.9). This system of pressed polycarbonate units forming the arc was originally developed by Renzo Piano as polyester frames at Genoa, Italy, in 1964/1965.

End wall panels

Perhaps the most disappointing feature of the pavilion was the solid timber-panelled end walls (a client requirement) (Figure 12.10) made visually lighter by the use of mirrors internally to carry through the effect of the structure.

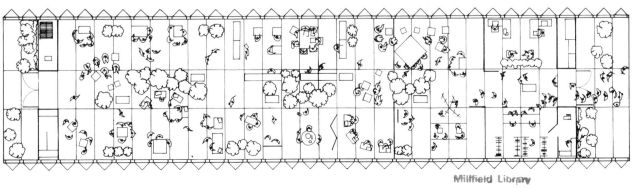

12.3.

Millfield Library
College of Technology
BELFAST

12.4.
Exploded view of fixing at apex of pyramid. 1 Stainless steel (Kinch) plate; 2 stainless steel washers glued to each side of the polycarbonate pyramids; 3 stainless steel rod with rubber block cast on; 4 aluminium node finger jointed to outer beechwood chord

12.5.
Fixing at apex of polycarbonate pyramid

12.6.
Exploded view of fixing at base of pyramid. 1 Stainless steel block glued to polycarbonate pyramid; 2 freely rotating cross pin; 3 200 mm long rod fixed to the cross pin at one end, a rubber block cast on the other; 4 aluminium node finger jointed to inner beechwood chord. Note that node is pinned to base plate

12.7.
Rods connecting polycarbonate pyramid to inner timber chords. Note anti-condensation air nozzle on duct between chords

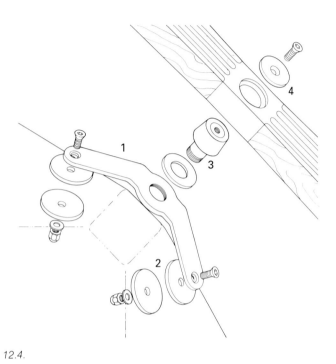

12.4.

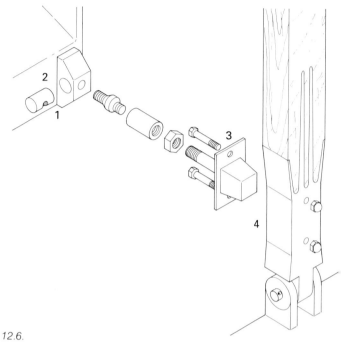

12.6.

12.5.

12.7.

12.8.
Pinned joint at base of arch

12.9.
Polycarbonate units with transparent PVC strip. Note fishtail air ducts

12.10.
Timber-panelled end walls. Note also at top of arch vein ducts branching off main spine duct

Services

All services were originally intended to fit within the floor space and exposed ducts were used to pass air between the services floor zone to the skin zone by means of 'fishtail' ducts (see Figure 12.9). It may be interesting to note the similarity of this method to that used by Richard Rogers at Lloyds of London, where a similar technique was used to pass the warm air through the glazed external walls.

In addition, condensation was controlled by passing small quantities of heated air onto the inner surfaces of the pyramids from aircraft-type nozzles from the 'vein' duct, which passes between the pairs of inner chords forming the arches from a central supply duct (see Figures 12.7 and 12.10).

Temperature control

The original concept of the transparent polycarbonate skin led to some problems from glare and heat build-up. To enable the internal temperature to be regulated, modifying devices comprising double-walled white insulated polycarbonate pyramids were fitted within the transparent pyramids. Additional thermal control and shading devices made from perforated aluminium panels were also used. A computer program had been developed to establish the thermal performance and to give the required heating and cooling capacities of the air-conditioning system.

References

Anon., Pavillon d'Exposition IBM, IBM Pavilion Pan 1984. *Architecture d'Aujourdhui*, 235, October 1984.

Dini, M., *Renzo Piano, Project and Buildings 1964–1983*, Architectural Press (now Butterworth Architecture), London, 1984, pp. 74–79. Describes early development of the 'electronic greenhouse' but the method of connecting the polycarbonate pyramids to the aluminium nodes was later superseded.

Hannay, P., 'Piano forte', *Architects' Journal*, 24 October 1984, pp. 24–27. Not a particularly useful technical reference but shows photographs of assembly of the pavilion at the Natural History Museum site in London.

Kinch, R. and Guthrie, A., 'The IBM travelling technology exhibition', *The Arup Journal*, **19**, No. 4, December 1984, pp. 2–6 (published by Ove Arup and Partners, London). By far the best source of information on the development of the structure and services, with clear photographs of the connection joint details and anti-condensation air nozzle.

12.8.

12.9.

12.10.

Johnson and Johnson World Headquarters, New Brunswick, New Jersey
Architects
I.M. Pei & Partners

General

This office complex, built in 1982 for Johnson and Johnson Inc., is situated within a 16-acre parkland setting, 501 George Street, adjacent to Rutgers University Campus in New Jersey, USA. The complex consists of a 16-storey tower linked to a series of connected four-storey blocks of offices. The tower, a modified square plan, and the serrated-shaped wing are clad in aluminium panels with continuous bands of clear glass (Figure 13.1). This early use of plate aluminium assembly is the main reason for its inclusion here.

The total floor area is 450 000 ft^2, of which approximately one third is contained within the tower and the rest in the serrated-shaped wing. Executive parking for 70 cars is located below the lawn fronting the tower, with space for a further 800 cars on the northern part of the site. The main contractors were John W. Ryan Company, NYC and the panel fabricators were Trio Industries. The total project value was $76 500 000.

13.2.

13.1.

13.1.
General view

13.2.
Aluminium panel fixed back to
concrete frame

13.3.
Sequence of assembly

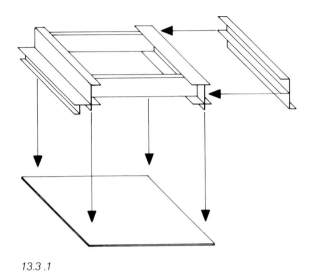

13.3 .1

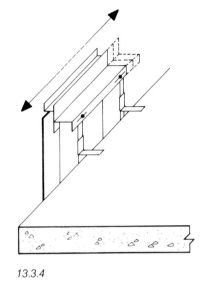

13.3.4

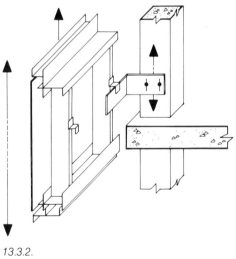

13.3.2.

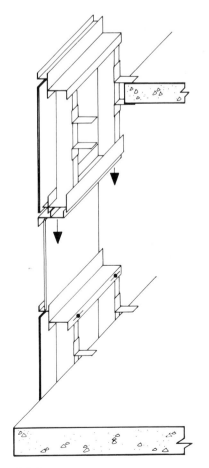

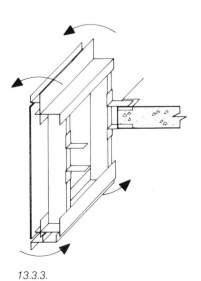

13.3.3.

13.3.5.

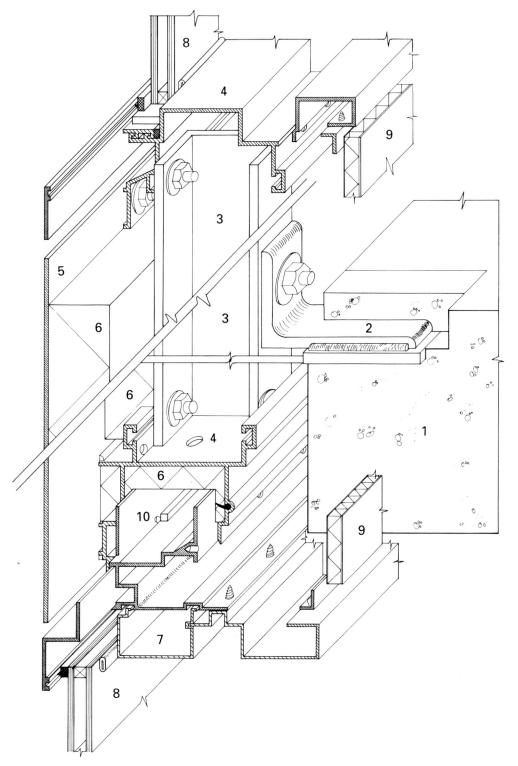

13.4.

13.4.
Sectional axonometric of fixing to slab. 1 Concrete floor slab; 2 steel angle site welded to steel inset cast into slab; 3 vertical member of panel frame; 4 horizontal member of panel frame; 5 4.5 mm thick aluminium sheet panel; 6 mineral wool insulation; 7 window head retainer; 8 double-glazed panel; 9 internal lining board; 10 weepholes

13.5.
Detail of horizontal joint. 1 4.5 mm thick aluminium sheet panel; 2 Silpruf seals; 3 weepholes and baffle in upstand gutter; 4 neoprene wipe seals; 5 back-up gutter section at top of panel; 6 9 mm diameter weeptube

13.6.
Aluminium top-hat section between aluminium sheets forming a false joint. 1 4.5 mm thick aluminium sheet panels; 2 Silpruf seals; 3 extruded aluminium top-hat section; 4 stiffener section

13.7.
Detail of glazed unit cill. 1 4.5 mm thick aluminium sheet panel; 2 double-glazed window unit; 3 Silpruf seal; 4 weepholes; 5 vertical member of panel frame; 6 internal lining

Cladding

Figure 13.2 shows the 4.5 mm sheet aluminium panel, colour off-white, mounted on an extruded aluminium framed fixed back by cleats to the concrete floor slab. The sequence of assembly (Figure 13.3) was as follows:

1. The panel sheet was bolted to the aluminium frame and a window head retainer was screwed to the bottom horizontal member for transportation.
2. A temporary bracket was fixed to the columns and the height of the window cill was corrected. Cleats were then bolted to the frame uprights in a corresponding position.
3. Alignment of the panel was then set and the cleats were welded to steel insets in the slab.
4. The panel was positioned horizontally by sliding the panel sheet and horizontal rails against the stationary verticals.
5. The window was positioned and the head restraint was released down onto it. Glazing strips and seals were then attached.

Mineral wool insulation was mounted *in-situ* within the panel frame and an internal lining board was fixed to the rear face (Figure 13.4).

The detail of the horizontal joint (Figure 13.5) shows the back-up drainage system using an upstand gutter with weepholes to discharge any water penetrating the neoprene seals at the base of the panel. An unusual feature of the design is a 3 mm thick gutter section at the top of the panel mounted between the vertical frame members, which also drains any water entering the panel past the Silpruf sealant down to the base of the panel via a 9 mm diameter weeptube. It was this obsession with self-draining systems which typifies the US aluminium curtain walling systems of the early 1980s, possibly because of the lack of confidence in long-term durability of the available sealants and gaskets.

Another interesting feature of the design is the false joints formed between the 5 ft high infill panel and the 2 ft 2½ in top infill panel making up the total height of panel assembly of 7 ft 4 in, including the joint. This was formed using an aluminium top hat bolted to the inner side of the aluminium outer sheet (Figure 13.6). This may have been used for aesthetic reasons, but it is more likely that 5 ft was the maximum width of plate aluminium available.

Windows

Double-glazed window units are mounted back into a similar aluminium framing member as the panels, which also includes weepholes below the glazing units (Figure 13.7).

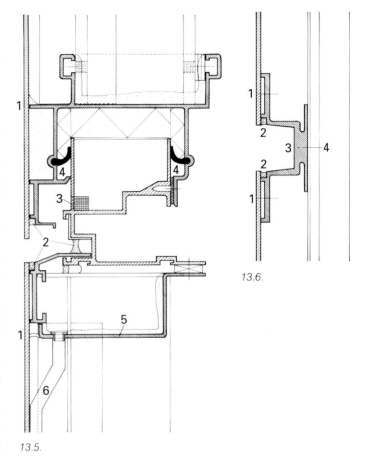

13.6.

13.5.

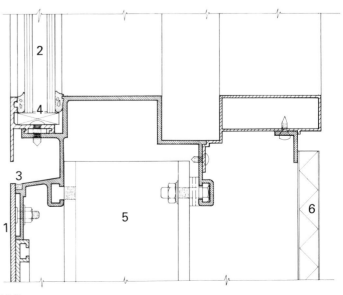

13.7.

14

Lloyds of London: Atrium
Architects
Richard Rogers Partnership

14.1.

14.1.
View of the Lloyds atrium from the south

14.2.
Detail of cast steel fixing bracket

14.3.
Atrium under construction

General

14.2.

As with the Hongkong and Shanghai Bank (Case Study 32), many articles have been written about the Lloyds Building and comparisons drawn between the two. The external cladding to the building has been described in Brookes, *Concepts of Cladding*, and this study is concerned only with the large atrium in the centre of the building with its prominent barrel-vault structure by Josef Gartner (Figure 14.1). Brief mention is also made of the staircase treads of the satellite service towers, which were formed by Nedal (Holland) and fixed by the Wessex Guild Ltd, this being one of the largest aluminium extrusions yet produced for the building industry.

Atrium structure

Although Lloyds was originally conceived of as a steel building, requirements for fireproofing eventually resulted in the use of a concrete frame. For the large glass enclosure of the full-height atrium, however, the fire-resistance requirements were less stringent and the preferred material could be used. Ove Arup and Partners were structural engineers for the primary and atrium structures. The main concrete columns, having performed their primary purpose of supporting the floors, extend up to the springing of the barrel vault to act as the main supports of the steel cage. The key component at this transition point from steel to concrete is a complex (two-limbed) cast steel bracket (Figure 14.2). These brackets thus form the bearing points for the steel structure, composed of a series of tubular lattices exposed on the outside of the building. The tubular arch lattices are supported on tubular steel triangular cross-section lattice beams which span between the concrete supports (Figure 14.3). Tubeworkers Ltd fabricated the atrium steelwork. The lattices use nodes of cast steel for bolting the steel members together, the cost of which was kept within reasonable limits by standardization of the members.

Cladding

The curtain walling is an aluminium-framed thermally broken carrier system fixed to the inner flanges of the

14.3.

tubular steel trusses (Figure 14.4). This supports the double glazing. A facility for a vertical cleaning track is also provided.

This is one of the few places in the building where a major component is not self-finished and maintenance-free. Elsewhere, stainless steel is used, but for the atrium it was decided to paint the structure, which is said to have a minimum life of 10 years before re-coating. A cleaning gantry is provided at the apex of the arch for external maintenance along which a crane runs. There is also an internal cleaning gantry at the springing of the arch.

One of the difficulties presented by the sequence of operations is that the large sheets of glass required for the curtain walling had to be fed between the exposed steelwork of the atrium and the concrete structure, and special tilting lifts were devised by Josef Gartner (Figure 14.6) to make this possible. Often the viability of a technical proposal is dependent on such ingenuity and experience of the fixing subcontractors, and architects would do well in understanding more of the means of assembly of components in building.

Services

A series of extract systems are used to draw up hot air from 'The Room', and the office above it, through the atrium by means of the chimney effect. These extract ducts are held by cantilevered steel supports connected to the triangular steel lattice edge beam and are expressed on the outside of the building.

Details

Although Lloyds is better known for the details of the external facade such as the 'fishtail' ducting (Figure 14.5)

14.4.
*Side and end sections through
atrium arch*

14.5.
Fishtail ducts and atrium structure

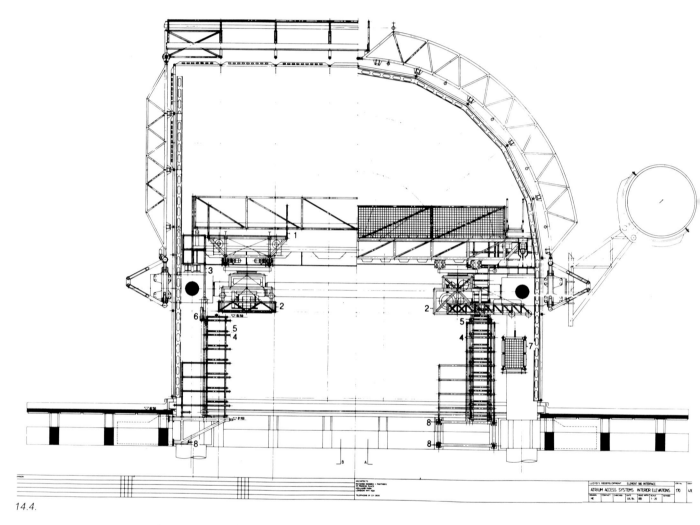

14.4.

or the fully assembled toilet modules by Jordans of Bristol, there are many less obvious examples of ingenuity in component detailing. One of these is the innovative use of large aluminium extrusions devised for the staircases of the satellite service towers. Rumour has it that Rogers, on visiting the Gartner works, saw the ends of a pile of square aluminium extrusions and suggested to job architects Frank Peacock and Amo Kalsi that these could be bolted together to form a system of aluminium staircase treads. On further investigation with one of the largest aluminium extruding companies in the world, Nedal (Utrecht), manufacturers of such products as yacht masts, flag poles and special extrusions for transport, it was found that the complete extrusion (requiring a die of approximately 500 mm diameter) could be made in one section (Figure 14.7). As a result, almost 2000 triangular profile treads, each the width of a staircase, were manufactured for this project and bolted to steel I-beams, which in turn were bolted to the *in-situ* concrete ramp which spans between floors (Figure 14.8).

14.5.

14.6.
Lifting equipment to offer double-glazed units up to frame

14.7.
Stair assembly

14.8.
Section through stair extrusion

14.6.a.

14.6.b.

14.7.

Once assembled, rubber stair treads with aluminium nosings were clipped to the aluminium extrusions forming the treads. Although very ingenious and appearing to satisfy the philosphy of component assembly, one could envisage simpler and therefore less costly ways of forming such a staircase assembly, as it would appear that the bottom member of the extrusion in the plane of the pitch of the staircase is duplicating the purpose of the slab below.

References

Anon., 'Two engineered solutions', *Architects' Journal*, 22 October 1986, pp. 79–94.

Brookes, A.J., 'Lloyds redevelopment, London', in *Concepts in Cladding*, Construction Press, London, 1985, pp. 75–80.

Davies, C., 'Lloyds: putting it together', *Architectural Review*, 1986, pp. 69–80.

Murray, P., *Lloyds of London*, Edizioni Tecno, 1985.

Russel, F., *Richard Rogers, Architects*, Academy Editions, London, 1985, pp. 130–133.

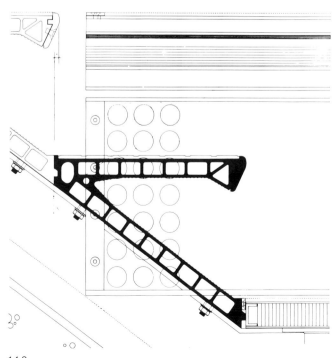

14.8.

Locomotive Shed, Preston Dock
Architects
Brock Carmichael Associates

15.1.

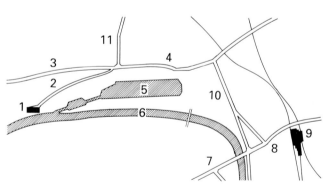

15.2.

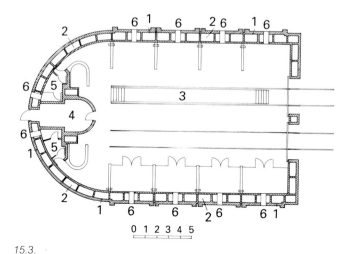

0 1 2 3 4 5

15.3.

General

Completed in 1986 for the Borough of Preston, in Lancashire, the new engine shed for the maintenance of the three locomotives that serve the Preston Dock was needed because extensive redevelopment of the Dock Estate for commercial and residential uses required the relocation of the dock railway (Figure 15.1). Located at the end of Chain Caul Road, Preston (Figure 15.2), the building provides both a landmark from the landscaped riverside walk and a visual end to the railway line. The architects decided to use traditional materials (bricks and slate) in a modern way to create a contemporary structure which, at the same time, would present an industrial image suitable for a railway building. It houses the locomotives with an inspection pit and lifting beam, toilet and shower facilities, mess room and supervisor's office (Figure 15.3).

Structure

The brick diaphragm walls with an external leaf of 215 mm and an internal one of 102.5 mm, separated by a 797 mm space, form a wall of 1115 mm total thickness (Figure 15.4). This supports a 675 mm deep precast concrete ringbeam on all walls. From this are sprung four 457×152 mm $\times$ 52 kg/m^3 universal beams with circular cutouts, supporting an arch-type structure made up from 219.1×10 mm c.h.s. with a 139.7×5 mm c.h.s. hoop above. Similarly, at the apse end, four $457 \times 152 \times 52$ kg/m^3 UBs support the circular end of the arch structure above. The whole structure is braced around the perimeter by 114.3×3.6 mm c.h.s. cross bracings with additional ties in the four square roof bays and in one bay of the main structure (Figure 15.7).

The roof is supported by U-section purlins spanning between the main UBs which, in turn, support the timber rafters, battens and slate tiles above (Figure 15.5). The whole structure is supported by a 250 mm thick reinforced concrete raft with a 600 mm deep perimeter edge beam.

Glazed lantern

The glazed lantern consists of Haywood's Patent Glazing (System 4672) at 610 mm spacing with 6 mm Georgian wire polished glass. The patent glazing sections span between an anodized aluminium ridge piece propped from the top of the c.h.s. arches and an upstand r.h.s. clad with anodized aluminium profiled sheet cladding (Figure 15.6). A continuous cleaning rail runs externally around the lantern upstand. It is this sophistication of

15.1.
View of gable wall

15.2.
Site plan. 1 Locomotive shed; 2 Chain Caul Road; 3 Riversway; 4 Water Lane; 5 Albert Edward Dock; 6 River Ribble; 7 Liverpool Road; 8 Fishergate Hill; 9 Preston Railway Station; 10 Strand Road; 11 Pedder's Lane

15.3.
Plan. 1 Diaphragm wall; 2 precast concrete ring beam above; 3 inspection pit; 4 mess room; 5 toilets; 6 high-level vents

15.4.
Half section half elevation of locomotive shed. 1 Diaphragm wall construction, 215 mm thick outer leaf, 797 mm cavity, 102.5 mm thick inner leaf; 2 precast concrete ring beam 675 mm deep; 3 Universal Beams, 457 × 152 × 52 kg/m³ with circular cutouts; 4 steel arch formed from 219 × 10 mm c.h.s.; 5 high-level extract duct; 6 114.3 × 3.6 mm c.h.s. bracing; 7 lifting beam; 8 inspection pit; 9 circular louvred air vent

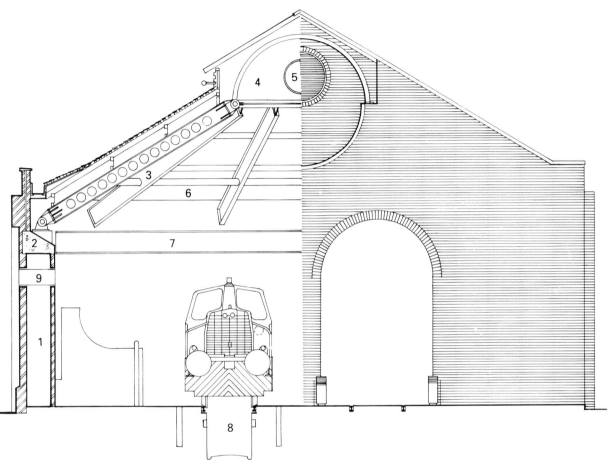

15.4.

detailing which characterizes the construction of the building.

Roof finish

The roof is composed of 457 × 254 mm Penrhyn Welsh slates on softwood battens, roofing felt, and 125 × 38 mm softwood rafters with 100 mm of mineral fibre insulation between. The rafters are firred at their ends to allow the rainwater to be discharged into a 400 × 400 mm pressed steel gutter supported by timber battens, which in turn restrain the parapet wall throughout its length at 1 m above its base (see Figure 15.5).

The brick walls

The exterior brickwork is mainly Blockley's Brindle Mix XVIII laid in Flemish bond. Nori Best Red Smooth facing

bricks, manufactured by Accrington Brick and Tile Company Ltd and supplied as Procter and Lavender Red Smooths, are used for feature bands and arches. The interior is given a light, airy feel using Smooth Lumley Buffs (stretcher bond) with complementary detailing in Procter and Lavender Reds. Lumley Buffs are also used for the exterior plinth.

Other external features include four 215 mm deep arch details bonded to each side wall centred on bullseye ventilation openings (Figure 15.7). The front gable wall features two arched entrances and a central inverted arch at the apex of the gable: this required the use of permanent polystyrene foam formers above the ring beam. Twenty-five millimetre Jablite expanded polystyrene forms the wall insulation fixed to the inner leaf with cavity straps, the whole assembly being built from the inside outwards.

15.5.
Gutter detail. 1 Cavity parapet wall; 2 precast concrete ring beam; 3 diaphragm wall; 4 steel bracket bolted to ring beam; 5 Universal Beams, 457 × 152 × 52 kg/m^3 with 244 mm diameter cutouts; 6 cross bracing; 7 steel channel purlins; 8 125 × 38 mm rafters firred at gutter ends; 9 100 mm mineral fibre insulation; 10 400 × 400 mm pressed steel gutter

15.6.
Lantern detail. 1 Haywood patent glazing; 2 aluminium ridge piece propped off c.h.s. arches; 3 high-level extract duct suspended off c.h.s. arches; 4 anodized aluminium profiled sheet cladding; 5 cleaning rail

15.7.
Site-progress photograph showing roof steelwork

15.8
Model of locomotive shed

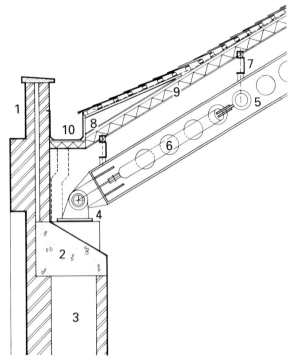

15.5.

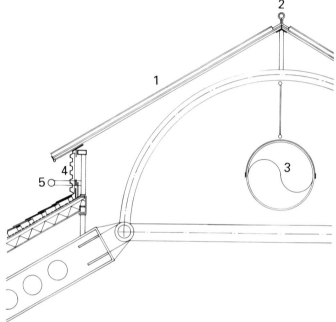

15.6.

Services

An ingenious system of exhaust and extraction is slung below the main roof structure. Designed by Rodney Environmental Consultants, the system is basically in three parts. First, a high-level general extract system is connected to a large circular louvre on the front facade. Second, a local high-pressure system is attached to the locomotive exhaust and ducted to circular louvres on the sides of the building. Two additional circular louvres with adjustable blades on the same elevation are used to equalize the pressure within the building. Finally, a gas-fired Reznov warm-air system is distributed by header ducts along each side of the building. Additional heating and low-pressure hot-water coils are provided in the maintenance pit and the small office and rest-room areas.

Lighting is sodium and electric services are also provided to a fixed beam to allow transverse lift of motors for inspection and maintenance.

References

Hetherinton, R. and Jamieson, B., 'The locomotive shed at Preston Dock', BPA Engineers File, Note No. 4, November 1986.

Marsh, P., 'Brick Development Association structural brickwork awards', Building Design (Bricks Supplement), 1986.

Ostler, T., 'Practice profile', The Architect, May 1987, pp. 47–50.

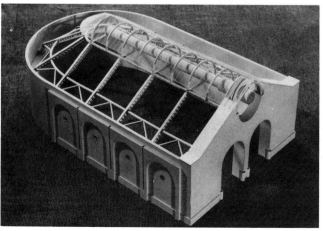

15.7.

15.8.

16

The Menil Museum, Houston, Texas
Architect
Renzo Piano

General

This museum was built to house the De Menil Collection of Modern and African Primitive Art in Montrose, Houston, Texas, USA (Figure 16.1). A close friend of the client, Pontus Hulten (Director of the Pompidou Centre's Art Museum), suggested Penzo Piano as the architect, and after a trip to Israel in late 1980 the idea for a museum where the use of controlled daylight to illuminate the display objects was first suggested. Although modified since the first proposals, the design concepts of Renzo Piano with Peter Rice and Tom Barker from Ove Arup and Partners were developed in association with Richard Fitzgerald Partners, Architects.

Occupying an entire city block (Figure 16.3), the museum with its module of 40 × 20 ft comprises a rectangle 402 × 142 ft with a maximum height of 45 ft. The visual theme of grey clapboard with white trim and black canvas awnings resulted from the client's requirements, but it is the platform roofs with their elegant leaf shapes that makes the Menil Museum more than just a simple box (Figure 16.2).

Roof baffles

Natural lighting without glare is achieved by Piano's ingenious roof formed from ferrocement leaves hanging from ductile iron trusses. The whole character of the building is determined by this elegant organic roof structure which has an uninterrupted span of 12 m (40ft grid) across the bays (Figures 16.4 and 16.5). The ferrocement leaves were individually cast on a concrete formwork by Ferrocement Laminates Ltd of Leeds, specialists in concrete boat building. The underside of the leaf was hand finished while the top surface remained with its moulded form. The leaves were then bolted to a ductile iron (spheroid graphite) frames (Figure 16.6), which were made by North American Foundries Co., (and not Crown Foundry, as reported by Glancey). These frames were cast as individual triangular units which were bolted together and connected to the leaf to form 10 triangular truss bays spanning the complete 12 m. These frames were then fixed to trusses spanning across the 20 ft grid which also support the

16.1. General view

16.2.
Section through gallery

16.3.
Site plan. 1 Public entrance; 2
staff entrance; 3 temporary
exhibition gallery; 4 permanent
exhibition gallery; 5 conservation
laboratory; 6 staff lounge; 7
registration; 8 reception; 9 shop;
10 library; 11 orientation; 12 cafe;
13 administration

16.4.
Section across museum

16.5.
Internal view of gallery

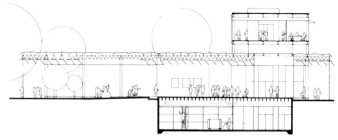

16.4.

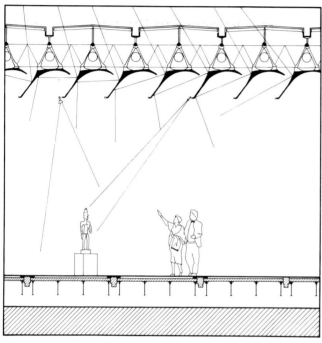

16.2.

16.5.

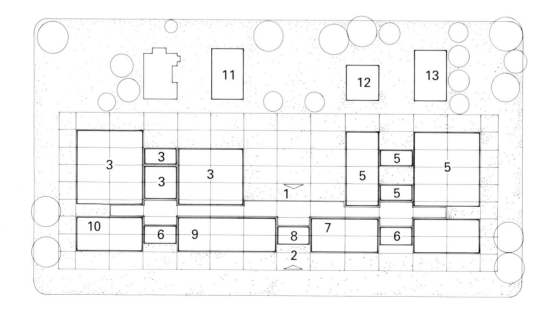

16.3.

16.6.
Exploded isometric of leaf and
frame. 1 Steel reinforcement; 2
cast-in spigots to take bolts; 3
concrete leaf; 4 cast-steel truss
members; 5 connector pieces

glazed roof above. A common misunderstanding is that the ferrocement louvres are adjustable – this is not the case. They act simply as reflectors to diffuse the light and prevent direct sunlight entering the building. Their shape has been derived from the sunlight conditions in Houston.

The shape of the leaves evolved from months of study, involving specific properties of materials, structural behaviour and optimum lighting angles. According to *Progressive Architecture*, the initial concept was of leaves in the form of flattened quarter circles connected by a truss derived from the Arverdi tubular system. The final shapes were developed by computer-generated modelling and actual physical mockups (see *PA News Report*, September, 1982, p. 40). Dini's book on Renzo Piano's projects and buildings shows him in work sessions with Peter Rice and Tom Barker on his full-scale mockup of a typical exhibition room to study the true latitude of Houston, the results of research carried out previously on 1:10 scale models using theoretical mathematical analysis. It is this combination of design engineering and research that is so essential for the development of sophisticated component technology.

Piano has always been known for his interest in the craft of building related to the production of sophisticated components, and it is the choice of what are essentially traditional moulded materials (i.e. concrete and cast iron) which makes this assembly so interesting for students of the technology, and shows that architects need not be constantly looking for new materials (polycarbonates, etc.) but can use appropriate techniques to solve specific problems.

References

Anon., 'The responsive box', *Progressive Architecture*, May 1987, pp. 87–97.
Anon., 'Museo Menil, Houston', *Domus*, No. 34, August 1987, pp. 33–42.
Dini, M., *Renzo Piano, Projects and Buildings 1964–1983*, Architectural Press (now Butterworth Architecture), London, 1985, pp. 272–303.
Glancey, J., 'Piano pieces', *Architectural Review*, May 1985, pp. 59–63.

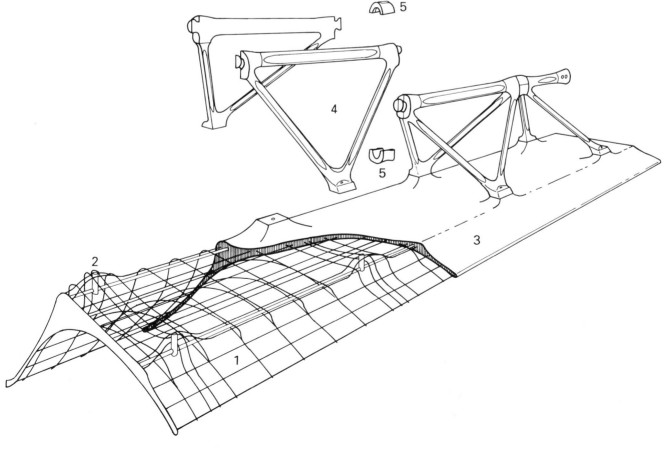

16.6.

17

Museum at Kempsey, New South Wales
Architect
Glenn Murcutt

General

Murcutt has been described by Alison Smithson as a 'timber and tin Miesian', and this building clearly displays his rational approach to building construction using low-cost materials such as corrugated steel roofing sheets to achieve an architectural simplicity. This building can be seen as a forerunner for his later work in Sydney (see *Architectural Review*, July 1987).

The museum at Kempsey, New South Wales, Australia, built in 1981, comprises three linked pavilions with vaulted roofs in corrugated steel (Figures 17.1 and 17.2). Light plays an important role in the design, with roof lights above the north pitch of the museum hall and in the smallest theatre pavilion (Figure 17.3). In order to control the internal temperature during the summer months, another characteristic of the design is the overlapping of the upper vault sheets. In addition, thin adjustable vents are provided along the tops of each wall, and two rows of rotary turbine vents either side of the central roof ridge exhaust stale air from the top of the building and form part of its character.

Structure

This is set out on a 4 m square grid (Figure 17.4), with tubular steel columns and bow-type trusses, whose bottom tension chords also support the centrally positioned fluorescent light fittings. The plate connector between the column and purlin has been deliberately enlarged to express its function. Below these purlins and spanning onto the loadbearing side walls a series of 100 × 38 mm pine rafters support the glazing where provided. Elsewhere, a secondary sheet of corrugated steel spans between purlin and wall.

Cladding

Roofs are a double skin of corrugated Lysaght 66 Zincalume, fixed with self-drilled screws and neoprene washers to mild steel Z-purlins at 900 mm centres (Figure 17.5). Insulation stops 50 mm clear at the purlins to allow air movement between the corrugations. The walls are 150 × 25 mm cedar panelling over 75 mm Insulwool, fixed back to the loadbearing brick walls. A glass block screen is positioned in front of the toilet block.

References

Bec, H., 'Detailing, national identity and a sense of place in Australian architecture', *UIA – International*

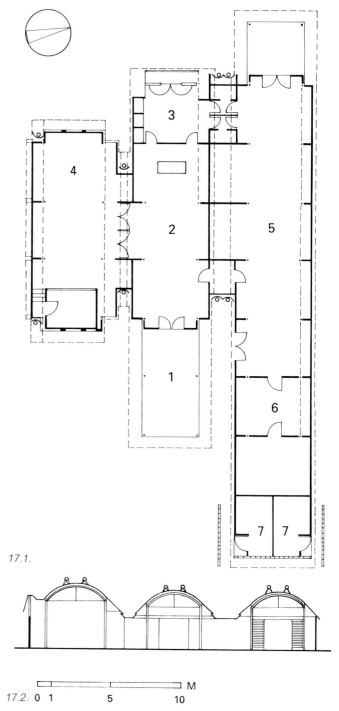

17.1.

17.2. 0 1   5   10   M

Architect, Edition 4, 1984, pp. 16–17.
Ogg, A., *Architecture in Steel – the Australian Context*, Royal Australian Institute of Architects, 1987.
Pegrum, R., *Details in Australian Architecture*, RAIA Education Division, 1984, pp. 16–17.
Spence, R., 'Museum boundaries', *Architectural Review*, February 1984, pp. 45–47.

17.1.
Plan. 1 Entry porch; 2 tourist information; 3 staff office; 4 theatre; 5 museum; 6 office and workshop; 7 public toilets

17.2.
Section

17.3.
Section through one pavilion. 1 Roof vents; 2 89 mm diameter c.h.s. curved to roof profile; 3 steel tie rod; 4 300 × 50 mm timber fascia beam; 5 brick wall; 6 mild steel Z purlins; 7 corrugated steel roofing with inner layer of corrugated ceiling lining; 8 600 mm wide steel through gutter

17.4.
Isometric of pavilion structure

17.5.
Detail of slat sunscreen. 1 75 × 3.2 mm aluminium louvres; 2 6 mm clear toughened glass; 3 aluminium glazing bars at 660 mm centres; 4 100 × 38 mm pine rafters under each glazing bar; 5 89 mm diameter c.h.s. lining; 6 150 mm mild steel Z-purlin; 7 insulation; 8 corrugated steel roof fixed with self-tapping screws

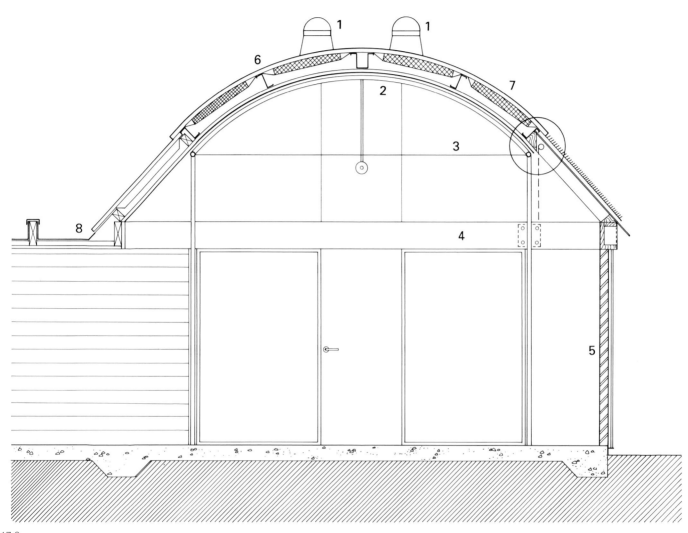

17.3.

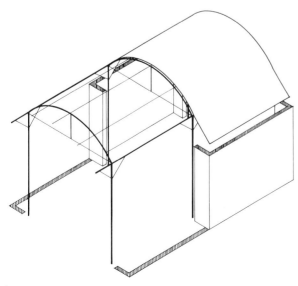

17.4.

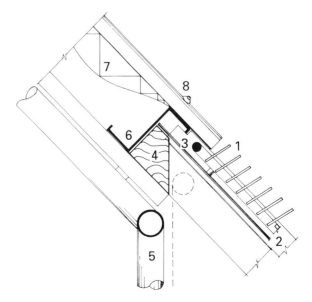

17.5.

Oculenti Contact Lens Factory, Holland
Architect
Thijs Asselbergs

18.1.

General

Situated in north Hoofddorp near Amsterdam in Holland (Figure 18.1), this small factory by architect Thijs Asselbergs was completed in October 1985. It was built for a small manufacturer of contact lenses, and the square-plan building consists of office accommodation on the ground floor, comprising directors' offices, reception, general offices and central toilets, with a top-lit central staircase leading to the first-floor workshop areas, canteen and meeting room with stacked toilet unit.

The building has a modern image, complete with corner details obviously influenced by Mies van de Rohe's ITT building in Chicago (Figure 18.3). With a floor area contained within the square grid of ten bays each measuring 1.64 m, and an elevation of six bays each measuring 1.04 m all carefully designed around a grid, the building represents a clear demonstration of dimensional coordination (Figure 18.2).

Structure

The building appears to be supported by two box-like structures cantilevered from four masts, forming a square at the centre of the buildings. In reality, the ground floor comprises a precast concrete-framed structure (Figure 18.4) onto which the steel frame has been mounted. This probably has resulted from the building-

18.1.
General view

18.2.
Elevation, section and plan. 1.
Reception; 2 offices; 3 store
room; 4 staff entrance; 5 meter
cupboard; 6 toilets; 7 fitting room;
8 lens production; 9 meeting
room; 10 canteen; 11 services; 12
air lock

18.3.
Comparison of corner details. (a)
Asselbergs. (b) Mies van der
Rohe

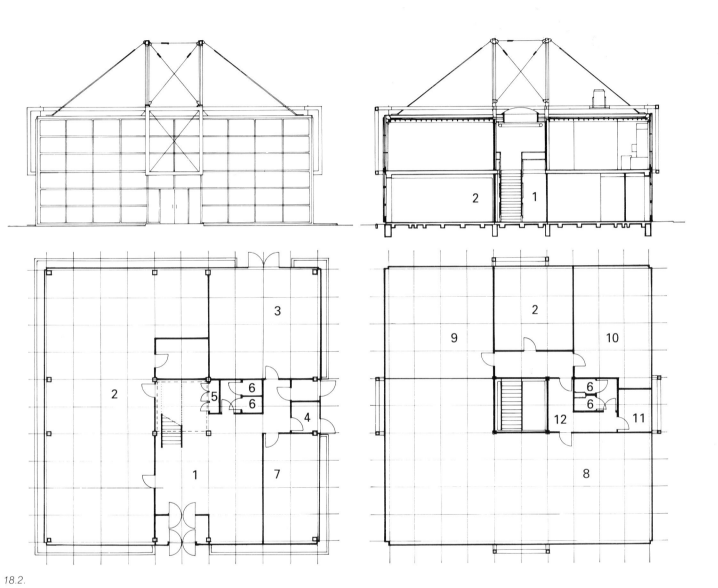

18.2.

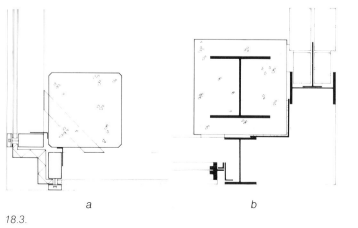

a   b

18.3.

control requirement allowing single-storey unprotected
steel frames (Figure 18.5).

The ground floor concrete ring beam supports a series
of precast concrete flooring units. The frame and the
first-floor slab are formed in reinforced concrete, with
four concrete columns set 3.28 m apart, defining the
central square of the building. These central columns
continue as steel r.h.s. section which are cross braced
together, and a frame consisting of four pairs of steel
H-beams, 210 mm square and 3.28 m apart, are welded
to them and have cantilevered supports from the floor
slab at the edge of the building. These vertical supporting frames are cross braced with steel cables (Figure
18.6).

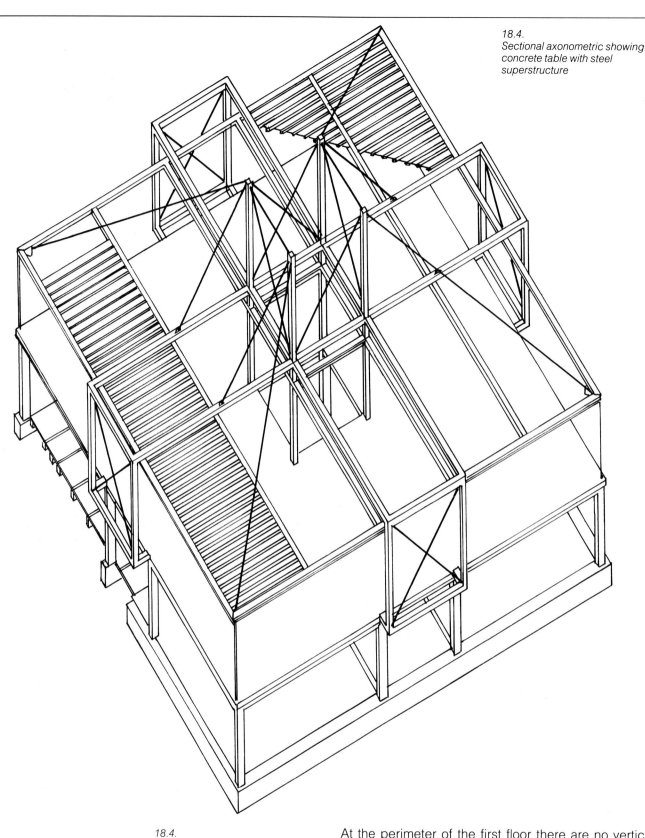

18.4.
Sectional axonometric showing
concrete table with steel
superstructure

18.4.

At the perimeter of the first floor there are no vertical columns, the roof edge beams being supported at their ends and one-third intervals by suspension cables, in the centre two points by the box frame and at their corners from the central masts. The corner junctions of the edge beams are also tied to the concrete slab below. It was necessary to prop these edge beams during construction prior to installation of the tension links.

Cladding

The cladding consists on both ground and first floors of a simple curtain walling section fixed at the head and base to the supporting structure. The black-finished aluminium

18.5.
The building under construction

18.6.
Section through the building. 1
Concrete foundations; 2 concrete
table; 3 steel members supported
off concrete base

18.7.
Eaves detail. 1 Steel
superstructure; 2 adjustable steel
hanger; 3 roof membrane; 4
concrete roof tile propped on
rubber pads to allow drainage of
rainwater; 5 22 mm thick plywood;
6 perimeter steel channel; 7 steel
beam; 8 profiled steel sheeting; 9
min. 70 mm insulation laid to falls

cover strips support sandwich panels of two skins of
3 mm aluminium and 35 mm of sheet polyurethane.
Double-glazed window sections also clip into the same
aluminium framework (Figures 18.2 and 18.7). One of the
classic difficulties of passing the framework through
external cladding is the joint around the projecting frame.
This has been resolved using a plate fitting around the
curtain walling assembly (Figure 18.9).

Roofing

Profiled steel roof decking spans 3.28 m in one direction
onto steel purlins suspended from the frame above. In
the central bays the suspension system was not required, as the purlins could span onto the central
columns. Above the roof decking is 70 mm of insulation,
with a continuous PVC finish. The roof drainage occurs at
the centre of the building adjacent to the central rooflight
and the drainage pipes are exposed below the ceiling at
this point (Figures 18.8 and 18.10).

Internal detailing

It is satisfying to see the component nature of this
building as expressed on the facade carried through into
the internal linings and fittings. Many of the American
examples elsewhere in this book, while expressing a
modular aluminium skin on the outside, use conventional
materials on the inside, and even Richard Horden, in his
Yacht House (see Case Study 30), was required to
provide plasterboard linings. In this case, however,
Asselbergs has designed his building to express the
nature of the construction, such as the soffits of the
galvanized metal ceiling and the curtain wall framing.
Designers seeking to create a similar constructional
purity should ensure that these hard finishes and
expressed services are to the client's satisfaction.

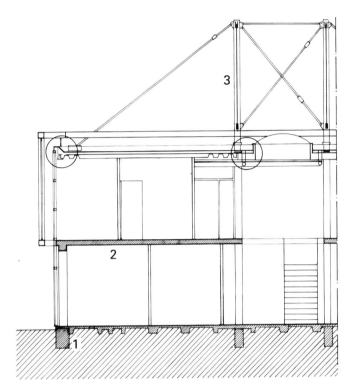

18.6.

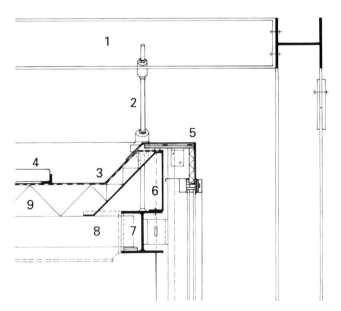

18.7.

18.5.

18.8.
Roof detail at skylight. 1 Steel superstructure; 2 roof membrane; 3 insulation laid to falls; 4 profiled steel sheeting; 5 insulated drainpipe in steel casing; 6 perimeter drainpipe running around skylight (see Figure 18.10); 7 metal capping; 8 2 m square clear acrylic double-skin skylight

18.9.
Steel frame projecting through cladding

18.10.
View of stairwell showing exposed drainpipes

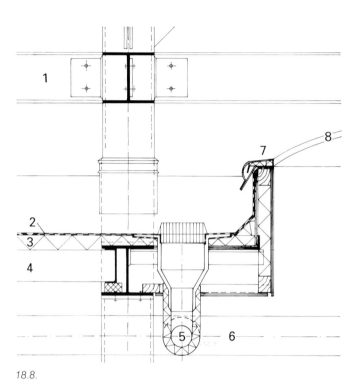

18.8.

18.10

References

Anon., 'Flexibiliteit leidt tot opmerkelijk bedrijfsgebouw', *Bouwwereld*, 13 December 1985, pp. 20–23.

Asselbergs, T., 'Bedrijfgebouw voor Oculenti', *Architectuur + Bouwen*, December 1985, pp. 17–20.

Van Heuvel, W., 'Een fragiele witte doos in Hoofddorp', *Architetur Bouwen*, December 1985, p. 21.

18.9

19

Operations Center for Philip Morris (USA)
Architects
Davis Brody & Associates

General

Located in Walmsley Boulevard, Richmond, Virginia, USA (Figures 19.1 and 19.2), this complex was designed for the makers of Marlboro cigarettes and comprises three linked pavilions clad with anodized aluminium panels and horizontal bands of glazing. A three-storey top-lit circulation route runs centrally through the administrative and research/engineering pavilions, and this is linked to the pilot plant building by a covered walkway which is finished in bright red. This colour is also used in the gateways which signal the entrances to the building.

The plan is arranged in 10 m bays around the circulation spine, offices enclosed in glass screens being located adjacent to the passage, allowing the open-plan areas to be situated next to the window walls. Semi-cylindrical stair wells, tubular balcony rails at upper levels and a careful use of colour create a pleasant enclosed street which unifies the diverse activities within the building.

One could compare the skin of this building with those of the Devonshire Building, Boston (Case Study 10) and the New Jersey Justice Complex (Case Study 23), all of which use aluminium panels. In this case, however, the architects have gone further in designing a coordinated facade system which incorporates its own environmental control mechanisms.

Cladding

The cladding (Figure 19.3), supplied and fixed by Zimmcor, Quebec, is mainly clear anodized 3 mm aluminium sheet, approximately 2 × 1 m, fixed to extruded

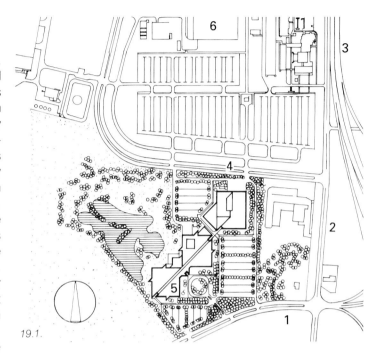

19.1.

aluminium mullions and transoms which are in turn fitted back to the main structure by angled cleats. The main spandrel panels consist of 3 mm plate aluminium mounted on an extruded aluminium frame with 75 mm fibreglass insulation and vapour barrier. These panels project approximately 170 mm from the front of the glazing with curved panels at the cills and parapet, which are finished in white fluorocarbon. The purpose of

19.1.
Site plan. 1 Walmsley Boulevard;
2 Commerce Road; 3 Interstate
95; 4 Bells Road; 5 Operations
Centre; 6 cigarette factory

9.2. Entrance elevation

19.2.

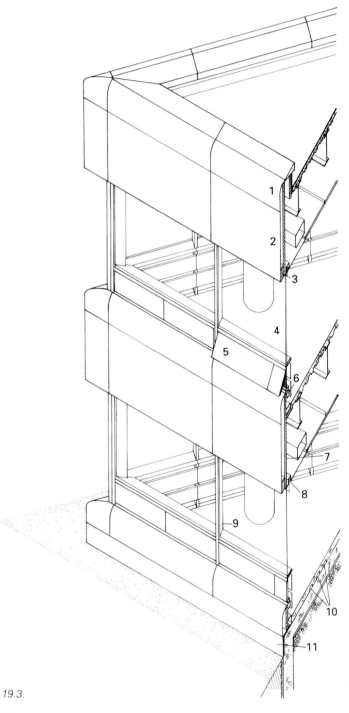

19.3.
Sectional axonometric through cladding. 1 White Kynar-painted aluminium trim; 2 clear anodized aluminium panel; 3 exterior aluminium venetian blind; 4 clear insulating glass; 5 operable vent; 6 fin-tube radiator; 7 insulation; 8 recessed motorized shades; 9 aluminium mullions; 10 power and telephone underfloor ducts; 11 natural cleft slate base

this additional space was originally to contain the outside sunshades which were later superseded by internal blinds. This modulation of the facade has some implication on the fixing screws to the joint cappings (see later).

In the same line as the windows, openable ventilation panels, also in aluminium, serve as a means of natural ventilation in the event of a breakdown of the mechanical air-circulation system (Figures 19.4 and 19.5). These panels are fabricated using two skins of 3 mm aluminium sheet with an aluminium frame and 50 mm of fibreglass insulation, top hinged to an extruded aluminium framing system mounted within the curtain walling assembly with a fixed aluminium mesh flyscreen behind.

The windows, 2 × 1.76 m double-glazed insulated units, are fitted within the curtain walling section in a way similar to the panels, using a pressure plate screwed to the mullions and transoms with an extruded aluminium snap-on cap (Figure 19.6). Face fixing of these pressure plates through the 12.5 mm slot between the projecting panels must have given some headaches to the fixing contractor (Figure 19.7).

The base of the building is faced with a small horizontal band of natural cleft slate edging to the concrete slab, allowing natural vegetation to be laid immediately adjacent to the facade.

The choice of white trim and dark anodized aluminium panels, while serving to emphasize the edges of the building, has two practical aspects. First, the curved corner pieces can be formed and post-coated in fluorocarbon and, second, any difference of colour matching, which is so difficult with anodized aluminium, is less obvious because of the bands of white.

Services

For energy conservation, the building was designed with exterior venetian blinds (also used in the Burrell Collection Building, Case Study 3). Supply problems delayed this installation and instead computer-controlled translucent fibreglass shades were installed behind the glass. The shades are automatically adjusted every 20 minutes for sun angle and desired sun penetration and heat gains. Heating is by perimeter fin tube and air-conditioning ducts are concealed above a suspended ceiling. The openable panels below the windows allow manual control in the event of a system failure.

In the skylight zones, air is moved by fans. Power and telephones are distributed in an underfloor duct system, with flat cables under the office carpets.

19.3.

References

Anon., 'Efficiency enriched and enlivened', *Architectural Record*, March 1983.
Anon., 'The staff gets the windows at Philip Morris', *Corporate Design*, November/December 1983.

19.4.
Detail of window cill and operable ventilation panel. 1 25 mm double-glazed unit; 2 185 × 65 mm extruded aluminium transom; 3 extruded aluminium snap-on cap and pressure plate, with weepholes; 4 ventilator panel consists of 3 mm aluminium sheet, 50 mm rigid fibreglass insulation, 3 mm aluminium sheet and framed flyscreen behind; 5 underscreen operator; 6 curved aluminium spandrel panel with 75 mm rigid fibreglass insulation

19.5.
Plan of joint between ventilator panels. 1 185 × 65 mm extruded aluminium mullion; 2 extruded aluminium snap-on cap and pressure plate; 3 ventilator panel consists of 3 mm aluminium sheet, 50 mm rigid fibreglass insulation, 3 mm aluminium sheet and framed flyscreen

19.6.
Detail of window head. 1 3 mm aluminium sheet spandrel panel; 2 75 mm rigid fibreglass insulation; 3 motorized shade blinds; 4 extruded aluminium snap-on cap and pressure plate; 5 25 mm double-glazed unit

19.7.
Detail of vertical joint between spandrel panels. 1 185 × 65 mm extruded aluminium mullion; 2 continuous 125 × 50 mm steel r.h.s.; 3 150 mm aluminium anchor angle cleats; 4 structural steel frame; 5 extruded aluminium snap-on cap and pressure plate; 6 3 mm aluminium outer sheet of spandrel panels; 7 75 mm rigid fibreglass insulation

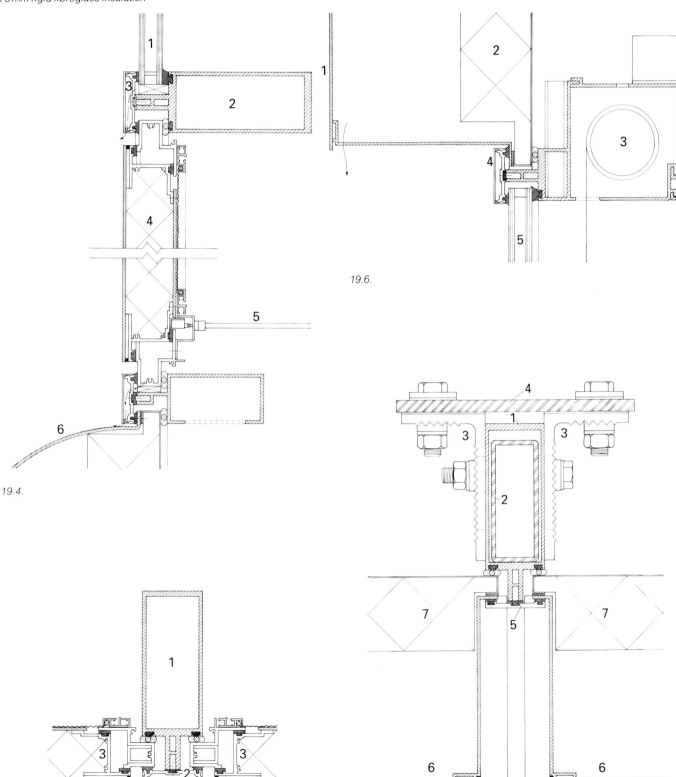

19.4.

19.6.

19.5.

19.7.

20

Parc de la Villette, Paris
Architects
Adrien Fainsilber and Rice, Francis and Ritchie

General

Completed in 1986, Adrien Fainsilber's conversion of the vast 270 × 100 × 45 m high abattoir into probably the largest scientific museum is, in many ways, a daring project. Four times the volume of the Beaubourg, the building rises from a sunken lake with three glazed bays projecting out over the surface of the water. Appropriately for a science museum, the stainless steel and glass structures are a showpiece of technology that tackle the problem of curtain walling with a radically different solution. Impressed by the quality of the glazed wall at Foster Associates' Willis Faber and Dumas offices, Fainsilber then worked in conjunction with Rice, Francis and Ritchie to make the structure of the glazed bays as light and transparent as possible (Figure 20.1). The whole assembly, including the stainless steel structure, was erected by CFEM.

Structure

Each of the three glazed bays on the south elevation is 32.4 m high by 32.4 m wide by 8.1 m deep. The 8.1 m square module forms the organizing principle for the primary structure, which is made up of stainless steel circular hollow sections. The main structure is braced along its top and sides by means of diagonal cross bracing in the plane of the structure. However, the main elevation is braced to the side elevations by a system of stainless steel compression struts and tension rods that act in a horizontal plane to counteract the wind forces (Figures 20.1 and 20.3).

Suspended glazing

In a conventional cladding system the cladding panels are supported off a secondary structure which, in turn, is fixed back to the primary one. At Parc de la Villette the secondary support system has been dispensed with: the glass is fixed directly to the primary structure and is provided with its own independent and much finer system of wind bracing (Figures 20.3(b) and 20.4). The structural glazing bay is an 8.1 × 8.1 m module subdivided into sixteen 2.025 × 2.025 m glass sheets (Figure 20.4). Each vertical row of four glass sheets is top hung and the load is taken on a central spring fixed to the top sheet. Every corner of the glass sheet is joined to the adjacent sheet by means of a moulded steel fixing with socket joints to allow movement in any direction. These fixings are restrained by the secondary wind bracing, devoted purely to the glazing. The glass sheets butt one another and the weathertight seal is provided by an *in-situ* applied clear silicone sealant.

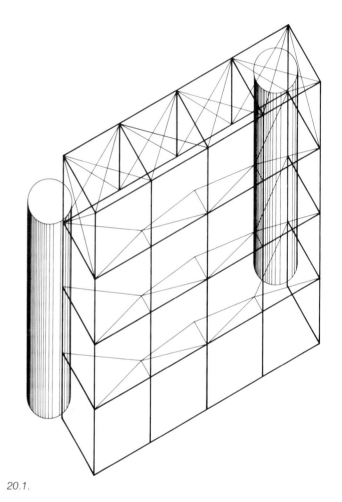

20.1.

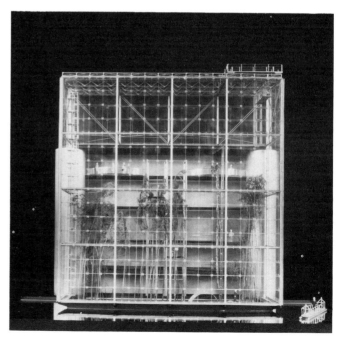

20.2.

20.1.
Diagram of structural frame

20.2.
Model of glazed bay

20.3.
Structural hierarchy (see also Figure 20.4). (a) Tension rods and compression struts bracing the primary structure. (b) Tension rods and compression struts providing wind bracing to glass sheets.

20.4.
View looking out through glass bay

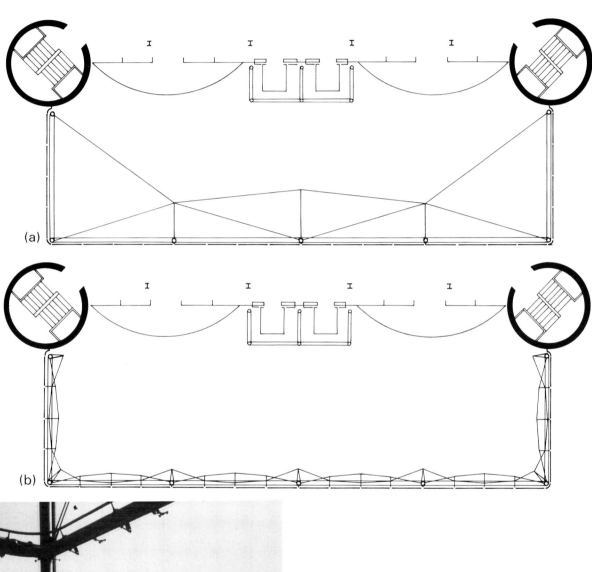

(a)

20.3. (b)

20.4.

75

20.5.
Glazing fixing arrangement,
Renault Parts Distribution Centre,
Swindon

20.6.
Glazing fixing arrangement, Lime
Street Station, Liverpool

The flexible form of structure makes use of the little-appreciated property of toughened glass, which can tolerate a large amount of warping. This property, coupled with the idea of making the wind bracing out of cables which had the advantage of being elements of pure tension, were flexible and very fine, all combined to achieve the transparency that was desired.

The system should be compared with that used by Foster Associates at the Renault Centre (see Brookes, *Cladding of Buildings*, Case Study 21), where 1800 ×

4000 mm glazing was restrained using spider connections back to 114 × 68 mm horizontal framing at 810 mm vertical centres. In this case the pick-up points on the glass were then in 1800 × 1330 mm bays (Figure 20.5). At Lime Street Station, Liverpool, a similar principle was used, mounting 1950 × 1050 mm glazing, in this case back onto vertical supports 205 × 135 mm at 1960 mm centres (Figure 20.6), i.e. fixing pick-up points in bays approximately 1900 × 1000 mm. At Parc de la Villette these pick-up points are approximately in bays 2 × 2 m

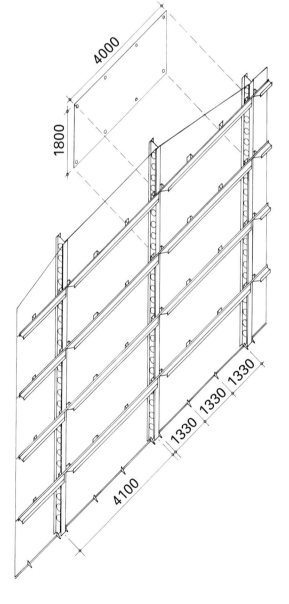

20.5.

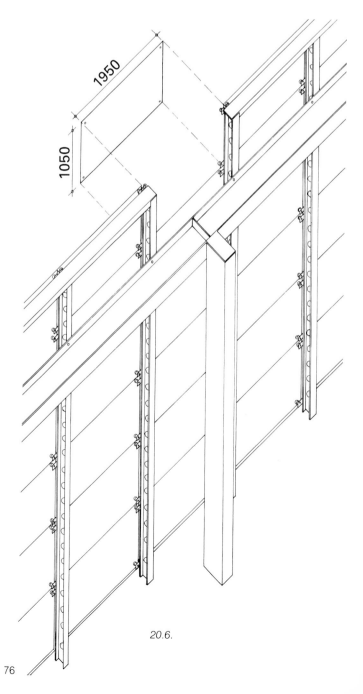

20.6.

20.7.
Glazing fixing arrangement, Parc de la Villette, Paris

20.8.
Exploded isometric of swivel fixing

(Figure 20.7). This demonstrates the gradual development of the technology, from the plate fixings as used at Willis Faber and Dumas to the drilled glass at Renault and Lime Street Station, with conventional fixing rails, to Parc de la Villette, with its tensioned fixing rails and a larger area of glass per fixing point and three-dimensional adjustment device.

Hanging four sheets of glass in this way induces stresses around the milled hole in the glass, of the order of fifteen times those in a single glass sheet. The innovative design introduces a system of swivels within the fixing that isolates the stresses and avoids any torsional stress, so that all the vertical forces are kept within the plane of the glass and horizontal forces can be taken out by the bracing (Figure 20.8).

Tests carried out on an 8.1 × 8.1 m sample proved the principle of the system, which literally breathed and flexed under positive and negative pressures producing deflections of up to 60 mm.

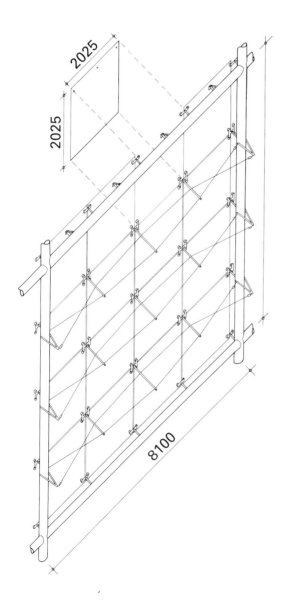

20.7.

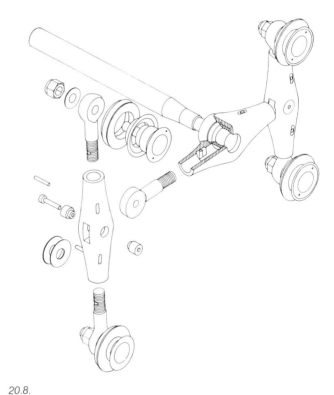

20.8.

References

Anon., 'Martin Francis – le discours de la méthode', *Architecture Ajourd'hui*, April 1986.

Ellis, C., 'Tomorrow's World', *Architects' Journal*, 30 April 1986, pp. 28–37.

Parsons House, London
Architect
Peter Bell and Partners

General

The Hall Place Estate, off Edgeware Road in Maida Vale, London W2, was completed in 1970 for Westminster City Council, and like so many high-rise, high-density schemes of this time, has proved an inadequate solution to poor housing conditions, mainly due to the poor quality of the infill panels, of cavity brickwork, and the cold bridge formed by the exposed *in-situ* concrete floor slabs (Figure 21.1).

The external fabric

The untreated softwood window frames had rotted to the point of failure by 1983, and the exposed concrete was spoiling around the reinforcement (Figure 21.2). Badly fitting draughty windows and inadequate insulation added to the problem. There was also a complete lack of any form of insulation. Peter Bell and Partners were asked to investigate repair work, but in their report of April 1983 suggested overcladding as an alternative. They proposed that, for an amount similar to that needed for the repairs, they could overclad the defective building in a rainscreen of aluminium-ribbed panels with insulation behind the new windows, which could be placed before the old ones were removed, thus minimizing disruption to the tenants (Figure 21.3).

For the final built scheme, completed in 1986, the architects consulted three cladding firms, and Hans Schmidlin (UK) Ltd was appointed cladding subcontractor, with Michael Barclay Partnership acting as structural engineers.

Structure

In overcladding, a series of support rails were first fixed to the existing structure with adjustable brackets. Because the brick infill panels were considered unstable, these rails had to be fixed between each floor slab, which required a fairly deep section. The architects decided to expose these cladding rails, and to use them as guides for maintenance cradle wheels (Figures 21.4 – 21.6).

The rails are made of extruded aluminium, 200 mm deep and 5.2 m long, with circular section outer flanges and channel section inner ones. The perforated webs reduce weight and aid air flow around the structure. Cutting the holes in the webs would, however, have increased their manufacturing costs, and it is doubtful whether this would in reality have offset the savings in main structure costs because of the reduced weight. The rails are fixed back to the concrete floor slab at each

21.1.

21.2.

storey by a pair of aluminium brackets, and vertical joints are formed by a spigot at the top of each tube which fits into the socket of the tube above. The aluminium used in the cladding structure is polyester powder coated with Colorsec (Figure 21.7).

Cladding

Cladding panels are hooked onto stainless steel support rods which span the U-section of the inner flange and they can be removed and replaced individually (Figure 21.8). The panels are also powder coated, 2 mm thick pressed (deep-drawn) aluminium with stiffened ends, profiled with a horizontal rib which is closed at the edge. Various sizes of panel were used, with widths of 480, 960 and 1440 mm. The edges are stiffened by folding back the sides of the panels, which are then perforated to form the hooks which clip to the support rods. The top and bottom panel edges overlap to prevent rain entering, but all-round ventilation is made possible by the fixing method.

21.1.
Parsons House before
overcladding

21.3.
Parsons House after
overcladding

21.4.
Cladding rails fixed to existing
fabric with adjustable brackets

21.2.
Deteriorated building fabric

21.5.
Insulation quilt fixed back to brick
walls

21.6.
Cladding panels hooked onto
rails

21.3.

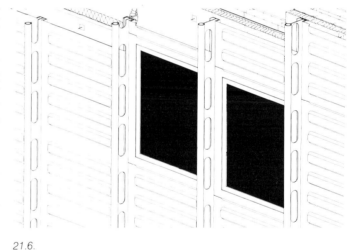

21.5.

21.4.

21.6.

The architects chose to use tilt-and-turn windows in aluminium sections, sealed back to the existing building with a waterproof skirt hidden by an internal timber lining.

The old walls are covered in an 80 mm thick blanket of mineral wool, fixed over the window infill panels with self-adhesive patent fasteners to prevent the need for drilling and fixing. This insulation covered all the cold bridge areas, isolating them from the outside.

The rails, panels and windows together form a rain-screen, which does not try to keep rain out altogether. Instead, any moisture trapped between the existing structure and new screen (both rain and condensation) drains down the ventilated gap at the back and exits through the open joints at the base of each panel. The mineral wool insulation is vapour permeable, but is not affected by water – it is also non-combustible. Note also the inclusion of cavity fire stops.

Under the terms of guarantee from the powder-coating manufacturers it is normal to require regular cleaning of

the panel surface. Cleaning and maintenance have been made easier by the provision of a permanent 'runway' for the maintenance cradle, raised on davits circling the entire building. The cladding rails act as vertical wheel guides.

The ground floor and first floor up to cill level has been tiled, with the new face finishing 280 mm forward of the existing structure (thus further forward than the overcladding). This allows the water behind the panels to drain out at their base into a concealed gulley. The cavity conceals the insulation, which is continued to ground level. The new tiles blend into the surrounding ground-cover, and are hoped to be vandalproof.

Comment

The Parsons House scheme is seen as a superior example of overcladding, which is a rapidly expanding construction method. The cost in 1986 of the overcladding system – about £220 per square metre – is seen by

21.7.
*Close-up of adjustable bracket
and cladding panel support rod*

21.8.
*Detail of cladding rail and double
glazing. 1 Cladding rail with
cladding panel support rod; 2
panel edge; 3 tilt-and-turn
double-glazed window*

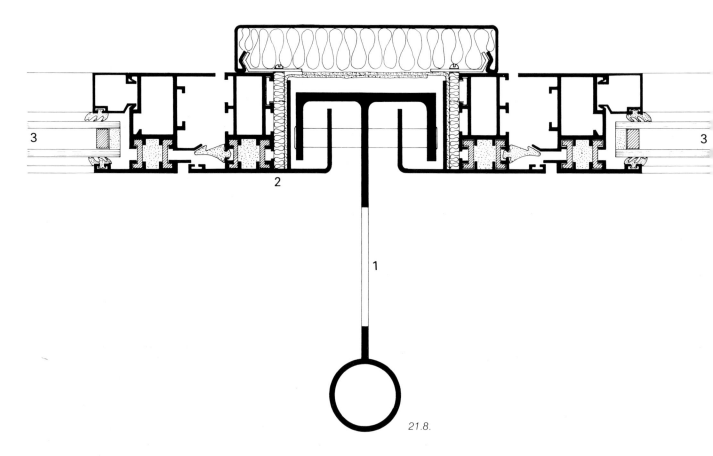

3   3

2

1

21.8.

21.7.

Roger Bloomfield of Bickerdike Allen Partners (building-failure experts and consultants to the architects) to be a long-term investment and therefore worthwhile. The cladding and windows should not require repainting for 40 years and the fuel bill has been reduced by 20%, as predicted. However, the panels and windows may require regular cleaning, and a stock of panels will have to be stored for potential future use since they are not standard designs.

References

Anon., 'A new suit of shining armour for decaying high-rise flats', *Aluminium Applications*, Summer 1986, p. 7.

Davies, C., 'High coverage', *Building* Supplement, 7 March 1986, pp. 8–11.

Harrison, H.W. *et al.*, *Overcladding – external walls of large panel system dwellings*, (BRE report) Case Study No. 1, pp., 52–53.

Pawley, M., 'New coat for a long life', *Guardian*.

Peter Bell and Partners, *Parsons House Overcladding*, Report to Westminster City Council (Client), November 1983.

Patscenter, Princeton, New Jersey
Architects
Richard Rogers Partnership

General

Patscenter is a new research facility for P.A. Technology, designed by Richard Rogers Partnership in Princeton, New Jersey, USA. It offers a high level of freedom of circulation, staff contact and maximum flexibility in the arrangement of offices, laboratories and services and the provision of a wide structural grid of totally free space. The client wished the building to have a strong visual presence that would emphasize P.A. Technology's innovative technical purpose. The architects responded by producing an expressive structure that is the antithesis of its neighbours in the think-belt around Princeton. The shock tactics of turning 'bland-box' inside-out are given maximum effect. By exposing the architectural images of science and technology the building provides an environment that seduces and stimulates a response (Figure 22.1).

Structure

The basic building concept is a central spine 9 m wide (Figure 22.2). The lower zone forms an enclosed glazed arcade providing main circulation, and above, slung on suspended frames, are the services plant. On either side of this spine two large single-storey enclosures, each 72 m long by 22.5 m wide, provide research space. To achieve the required flexibility these research areas are organized on a 9 × 4.5 m planning grid and are column free. All vertical structure within the building envelope is placed in the central spine (Figure 22.3). The large single-storey building with its general roof level only 4.5 m above ground level is enlivened by the deliberately dramatic steelwork frame with integral services (Figure 22.4).

The main structure, which is repeated at 9 m intervals, consists of a 7.5 m wide rectangular portal which acts as

22.1. General view

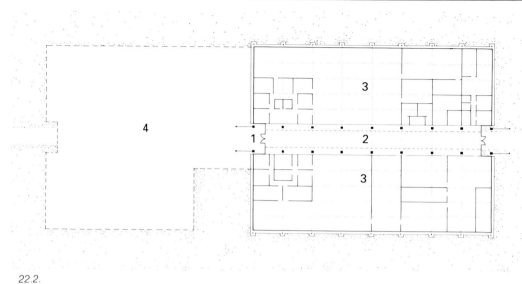

22.2.
Plan. 1 Entrance; 2 administrative spine; 3 research laboratories; 4 Phase 2 extension

22.3.
Isometric and section. 1 Administrative spine; 2 research laboratories; 3 bipod masts; 4 services platform

22.2.

22.3.

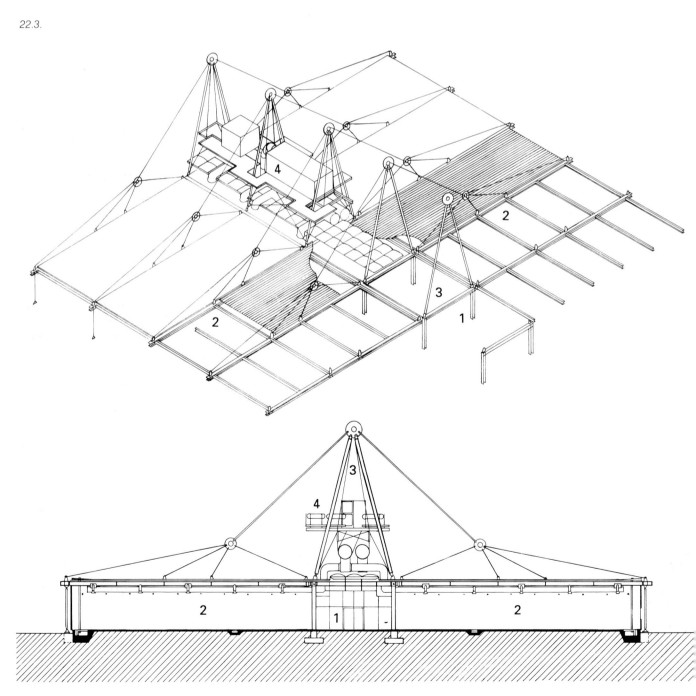

a base for the impressive 15 m high bipod mast. Inclined members are attached to the top of the mast to provide mid-span support for the main roof beam of the single-storey structure. The final form of the suspension system resulted after a long process of development and analysis. One problem in tension structure design is the effect of wind uplift: a perimeter column tie is needed to resist this. At his earlier building for Inmos in Cardiff, UK (see Brookes, *Cladding of Buildings*), Rogers used a V-shaped truss spanning from the central spine to the edge of the building. At Patscenter, although the span is much smaller, the truss is still required but it is less emphatically stated. When there is no uplift loading the two centre members supporting the roof structure are required to act as compression struts: consequently they are slender tubes. The two outer members act in tension and are rods. The structure is designed by Ove Arup and Partners.

One of the ways that the architects and engineers have managed to achieve a classic simplicity is the lack of diagonal bracing at high level between masts. Longitudinal stability is provided indirectly by making use of the suspended services platforms and their support hangers. As a result, the masts thrust upwards apparently independently, emphasizing the bay-by-bay flexibility of the building (Figure 22.5). Out-of-plane loadings on the masts and suspension systems are transmitted down to the main roof level, via the structural chassis of the services platform, then to ground level through the central portals and diagonal bracing at the ends of the building. Thus the building services help to justify the structure and vice versa. The overall weight of structural steelwork equates to 45 kg/m^2.

Cladding

Richard Rogers Partnership were keen to incorporate a large proportion of glazing into the wall cladding and yet conform to the insulation criteria set by the American codes. A successful compromise was achieved by the use of Kalwall translucent cladding. This system uses a sandwich made up of two light-transmitting fibreglass sheets bonded in an interlocking aluminium grid frame. To increase the thermal insulation of the panel gap between the two leaves, this was filled with translucent fibreglass inserts, their density selected to achieve the required insulation and light transmission. The overall panel thickness is 70 mm. The panels were prefabricated in 1.5 m wide and full storey-height frames to be erected on site.

The wall cladding provides a 20% clear glazing area, the remaining 80% Kalwall and a 17% light-transmission value and a 1.3 W/m^2°C U-value. The overall effect is

22.4.

22.5.

22.6.
Side view at night

22.6.

pleasing and similar to that of a translucent Japanese screen. (See the night-time view in Figure 22.5.)

Services

The planning concept of a central spine is ideal for the distribution of primary services and enables all the plant to be located centrally (Figure 22.6). Mechanical and electrical plant are in fact located at ground-floor level adjacent to the spine with air-handling and condenser plant on the suspended services platforms. The larger primary air ducts are external to the building envelope while smaller electrical and piped services are at high level within the spine. Secondary distribution runs laterally into the research enclosures.

Comment

This building is a pronounced refinement of its precursor for Inmos in Cardiff: solid-looking rectangular towers have been replaced by dynamic A-frames and complex joints have developed into simple geometrical 'washers'. The structure has achieved the inevitable simplicity that is the symbol of great architecture. A long, hard look at the structural principles and the solutions proposed is amply rewarded.

References

Gardner, I., 'Patscenter', *Arup Journal*, **21**, No. 2, Summer 1986, pp. 8–16.

Russell, F., *Richard Rogers and Architects*, Architectural Monographs, Academy Editions, London, 1985, pp. 44–45.

Sorkin, M., 'Another low-tech spectacular', *Architectural Review*, No. 1063, September 1985, pp. 38–43.

23

The Richard J. Hughes Justice Complex, Trenton, New Jersey
Architects
Grad/Hillier

General

This very large complex of law courts and tax offices for the State of New Jersey, USA, was completed in January 1982 at a total cost of $93.4 million. For such a project, two large architectural practices, the Grad Partnership of Newark and the Hillier Group at Princeton, worked together as the Grad/Hillier joint venture (Figure 23.1).

Built on an unusual chevron-shaped site, the overall design of the complex consists of an L-shaped office building with eight floors of accommodation and a ninth floor for mechanical services. The two equal wings of the L embrace the separate six-storey cube-shaped building containing meeting rooms, etc., which is suspended over a three-storey open-space mezzanine. The two parts of the building are separated by an atrium which begins at street level and rises the full nine floors of the building. Each of the cube's four floors are connected with the office accommodation by a series of bridges spanning the atrium space (two floors are two storeys high), which has structural silicone glazing with glass supporting fins.

Structure

The structural engineer was Daniel Sturn of Di Stasio and Van Buren. The most interesting aspect of the structure is the method of supporting the cube by four 7 m cylindrical columns 25 m centres apart, the load being carried on four trussed columns of structural steel within the

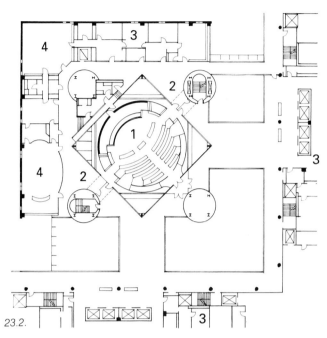

23.2.

23.2.
Plan of the central suspended cube housing the court rooms. 1 Court room; 2 lobby; 3 offices; 4 conference

23.1. General view

23.3.
Structural skeleton with columns, trusses and cube clad

23.4.
Structural skeleton with external cladding and atrium

23.5.
Exploded structural skeleton showing suspended cube housing the court rooms

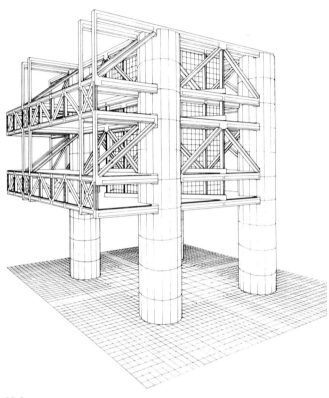

23.3.

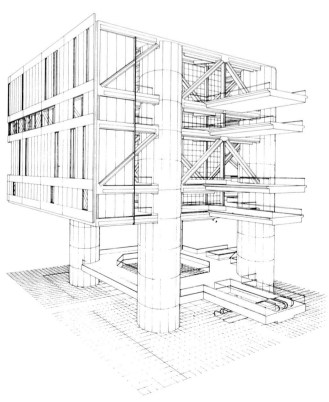

23.4.

23.5.

23.6.
Internal view of atrium

23.7.
Detail of window cill. 1 25 mm
thick double-glazing; 2 vinyl
thermal break; 3 hinged door for
natural ventilation with inset
screen; 4 site-applied sealant
with backing rope; 5 4.5 mm thick
aluminium plate with factory
welded Z-cleat; 6 75 mm thick
insulation; 7 gypsum board lining

cylinders. It is interesting to note the change of direction of these supporting I-section stanchions (Figure 23.2).

Four two-storey trusses intersect the columns at the second and fourth court building levels. These support two single-storey trusses at the exterior of the first court level and two on the third (see Figures 23.3–23.5). The main trusses have been exposed as a feature of the building, allowing people to walk through them (Figure 23.6). These approximately 9 m high trusses were sprayed to achieve a three-hour fire rating and then covered with aluminium. To some extent, this principle of fire rating can be compared with the Hongkong and Shanghai Bank by Foster Associates (Case Study 32).

Such large and complex trusses would require substantial welding, and to keep site welding to a minimum these were fabricated off-site, disassembled, transported and then reassembled on-site with bolted connections. The surrounding office buildings consists of a conventional structure with bays of 10 × 10 m.

Cladding

The exterior skin of anodized aluminium panels with horizontal bands of grey reflective insulating glass fabricated and assembled by Flour City Architectural Metals at a cost of $8 million represents a high standard of panel-to-panel curtain walling assembly mounted between the columns set back behind the facade and restrained at intervals by the floor slab. The 1.5 × 10 m panels consist of 4.5 mm aluminium plate on an extruded aluminium framework with 75 mm of USG Thermafiber insulation and an inner lining of gypsum board. The total panel thickness is 160 mm. It is interesting to note the method of fixing the framing to the plate aluminium outer panel, using a welded Z-cleat clipped into the extrusion with a space to allow thermal movement and a silicone joint factory applied between the two parts of the assembly. Thus the panel arrives on-site with the frame attached to it. A further weather seal is applied at the cill condition on-site (Figure 23.7).

Aluminium-framed double-glazed windows with solar reflective glass fit within the assembly with a total frame width of 160 mm (Figure 23.8). Continuous ventilation slots occur below the windows with a hinged cill-type section to allow natural ventilation. Also note the aluminium mesh insect screen mounted above the slots.

Another interesting feature of the assembly is the window-washing equipment, track mounted within the jambs of both the windows and panels, allowing access for cleaning gantries for both windows and anodized aluminium panels (Figure 23.9).

23.6.

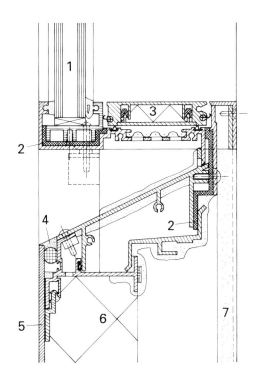

23.7.

23.8.
Window head detail. 1 25 mm thick double-glazing; 2 continuous polystyrene foam insulation; 3 hex head screws sealed at works; 4 4.5 mm aluminium plate with factory welded Z cleat; 5 75 mm thick insulation; 6 gypsum board lining

23.9.
Window jamb detail. 1 Track for window-washing equipment; 2 continuous vinyl foam self-adhesive tape; 3 thermal break; 4 25 mm thick double-glazing

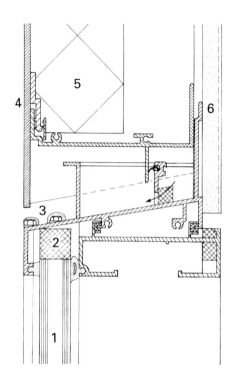

23.8.

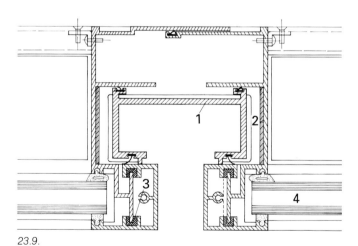

23.9.

Finishes

Generally, the aluminium is anodized and protected with one spray coat of Dupont 1234 clear laquer. This type of plate panel with welded stiffeners is difficult to manufacture, and it was the architect's requirement that these should be free of any bow or oil-canning, and that the stiffening rails should not 'read through' when installed in the building. The thickness of the plate (4.5 mm instead of the more usual 3 mm) would help in achieving the architect's specification for a maximum bow of 3 mm in 1 m. All columns are sheathed in the same aluminium that is used on the exterior and interior facades.

Mock-ups

With asemblies of this type it is necessary to provide a full-size mock-up complete with panels, openable vents, framing members, corner returns, window-cleaning guide tracks, spliced joints, sealants, glass and fixings, all with their correct finishes for the architect's approval. In this case there was an additional requirement for air- and water-penetration tests to be carried out by Construction Research Laboratory, Miami, Florida. Later modifications of the interlocking aluminium sections, designed to facilitate installation, resulted in the subsequent problems of air and water penetration in the completed building.

Costs

Costs of the structure represented approximately 20% of building costs, and mechanical services were of the same order. External walls were almost 9% of total costs with a similar allowance for the interior construction.

Services

In the interests of energy conservation, 172 solar collectors are located at 40-degree angles on the south side of the roof to heat domestic hot water. In addition to the top-floor mechanical services the building appears to depend upon the adjacent boiler plant in the nearby State Building as a source of heating and air conditioning.

References

Thomas, R., 'Unique design simplifies new justice complex', *Building Design and Construction*, June 1983.

24

Sainsbury's Supermarket at Canterbury
Architects
Ahrends Burton & Koralek

General

ABK won the 1982 limited-entry competition to design a new supermarket for Sainsbury's at Canterbury in Kent (Figure 24.1), which was completed in 1984. The brief reminded the competitors of the historic nature of the site, which was within sight of the medieval cathedral, and asked them to respect the local vernacular materials. It is perhaps surprising, then, that this masted and suspension cable structure of unashamedly modern design and materials should have won. In their entry, ABK claim that the masts echo the towers of the distant cathedral: they do in that they give vertical emphasis to an otherwise horizontal building, but the reader may feel that they have rather more nautical than ecclesiastical references.

The supermarket is on a difficult site on the Kingsmead Road and Northgate junction in Canterbury, with the River Stour bordering the western edge (Figure 24.2). The carpark is at the rear of the building, but because the road frontages are not owned by Sainsbury's and are to be built on, the main elevations of the building face the carpark.

The three functions of unloading, storage/preparation and sales are each housed in a separate structure of different length linked by service areas. Around these are grouped various offices, meeting rooms, etc., with the customer entrance located to the west of the sales area. Thus the building is composed of three blocks of masted structure linked by cross bracings over the 3 m service zone.

Structure

As the model shows, the roof structure of the largest of the blocks is composed of nine bays of paired 406 mm diameter c.h.s. mild steel columns supporting the mild steel main beams (356 × 368 mm × 153 kg/m I-sections) spanning 36 m. In the other two blocks, these main beams span 24 m. In all cases the beams are picked up by the suspension cables from the masts at 12 m intervals. The size of these paired mild steel rods is 60 mm diameter, and they connect to the beams via a 60 mm thick mild steel connector plate welded to the roof beams (Figure 24.3). Apparently there is no thermal break between the plate and the main beam.

Spanning 7.2 m between the main structural beams are mild steel purlins (203 × 133 mm × 25 kg/m) which

24.1. Model of competition design

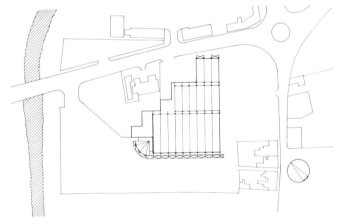

24.2. Site plan

support the lightweight roof composed of 70 mm profiled steel deck, supporting a vapour barrier, 40 mm insulation and 13 mm fibreboard covered with three layers of felt and chippings.

The reader should note the mild steel castings welded to the 60 mm diameter tie rods, and compare these with those used at the Victoria Plaza (Case Study 31) and by Richard Rogers in the Fleetguard Factory in France to observe the development of this type of construction. The method of connecting these plates to the beam connector plate using a stainless steel pin should also be noted (Figure 24.3). A low-viscosity silicone seal is placed between the plates and the cast ends of the rods.

The very lightweight roof deck would be prone to uplift

24.3.
Vertical section and elevation of connector plate. 1 60 mm thick connector plate welded to roof beam; 2 mild steel spade casting welded to 60 mm diameter tie rods; 3 60 mm diameter stainless steel pins with stainless steel pin cap; 4 low-viscosity silicone seal; 5 8 mm thick mild steel plate; 6 roof composition: three layers of felt and chippings, 13 mm fibreboard, 40 mm insulation, vapour barrier, 70 mm metal deck; 7 50 × 50 mm angle bolted to beam; 8 356 × 368 × 153 kg/m mild steel universal beam; 9 203 × 133 × 25 kg/m mild steel purlin

24.4.
Canopy suspended from outriggers

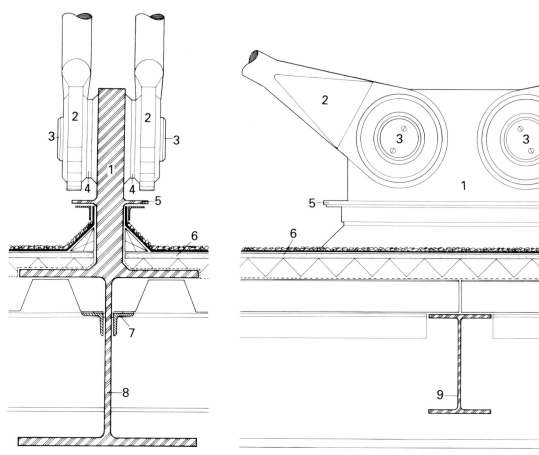

24.3.

24.4.

under certain wind conditions, but in this case the weight of steel supporting it is large enough to act as an anchor, thus eliminating the need for ties to keep the roof down. In addition, the main masts, with their projecting outriggers forming the compression member, support a fabric-covered ladder-type frame forming a covered canopy along the carpark elevation (Figure 24.4). These also link to a fan-shaped canopy with a fabric structure, suspended from its own mast arrangement.

Structural engineers for the competition scheme were Anthony Hunt Associates. However, the executive engineers were Ernest Green and Partners.

Cladding

Cladding to the sales floor block which faces the carpark is composed of 6 mm thick glazed panels and aluminium composite panels fixed to extruded aluminium curtain walling by Essex Aluminium. The interesting feature of this assembly is the cranked mullion spanning between

24.5.
Section through eaves detail. 1 168 mm c.h.s. mild steel outrigger; 2 plated steel connector between paired masts; 3 roof composition: three layers of felt and chippings, 13 mm fibreboard, 40 mm insulation, vapour barrier, 70 mm metal deck; 4 aluminium–polythylene–aluminium composite panel; 5 75 mm thick rigid insulation bonded to panel; 6 insulated panel; 7 extruded aluminium cladding mullion

24.6.
Section through roof and internal partition. 1 112 × 356 × 25 kg/m mild steel universal beam; 2 50 mm thick mineral wool quilt with wire mesh reinforcement and aluminium interlayer; 3 190 mm blockwork wall; 4 50 mm thick mild steel connector plate; 5 mild steel turnbuckle; 6 stainless steel collar over torched-on roof finish; 7 paired 406 mm c.h.s.

24.7.
Section through base of external cladding. 1 Paired 60 mm diameter tie rod; 2 precast paving slab; 3 6 mm toughened glass panel; 4 extruded aluminium frame with pressure plate; 5 paired 244.5 mm c.h.s.; 6 extruded aluminium cladding mullion; 7 stainless steel protection rails; 8 stainless steel angle; 9 30 mm thick terazzo tiles; 10 friction piles; 11 reinforced concrete perimeter beam

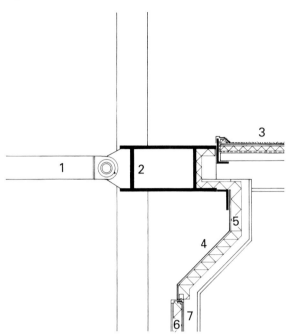

24.5.

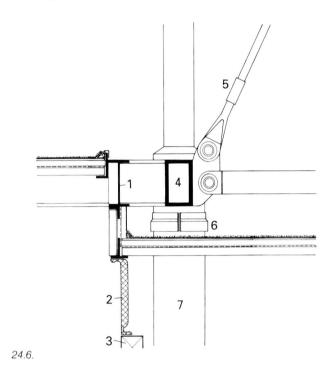

24.6.

the floor edge beam and the steel edge beam to the roof, into which are fitted cranked aluminium panels forming the recess at the head of the assembly (Figure 24.5). This recess is continued on all the blocks, but in these areas the walls have glazed 'Spectraglaze' concrete blocks. The purpose of the recess is partly to emphasize the roof plane and to act as a slip joint to take up the differential tolerances between the roof structure and external walls, which is always a problem with suspension structure of this type (Figure 24.6, 24.7). At the Renault Centre by Foster Associates a similar problem was solved using a neoprene skirt.

References

Anon., 'Canterbury choice', *Architects' Journal*, 13 October 1982, pp. 44–46.

Outram, J., 'Supermarket forces', *Architectural Review*, May 1983, p. 70.

Winter, J., 'Mast appeal', *Architects' Journal*, 5 December 1984, pp. 41–47.

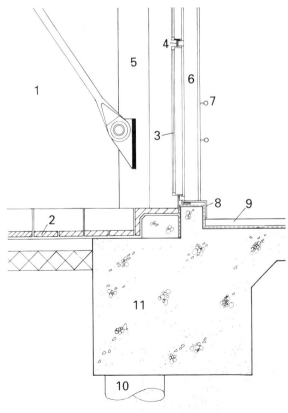

24.7.

25

Schlumberger Cambridge Research Centre
Architects
Michael Hopkins and Partners

General

Built in 1985 for research into rigs for oil exploration (which explains its section), the building is situated on the Madingley Road near junction 13 of the M11 west of Cambridge. With its cable structure, the project, designed by Michael Hopkins, Anthony Hunt Associates and Arup Lightweight Structures Division, represents the first large-scale example of the use of Teflon-coated glassfibre membrane in the UK (Figure 25.1). The shape of the building is determined by its use as an oil-drilling test station (Figure 25.2) and to ensure maximum contact between scientists of different departments.

The plan, composed of three central bays each 24 × 18 m, is defined on the east and west sides by five bays of office units with inset entrances dividing them (Figure 25.3). The building takes advantage of the contours of the site so that the test station and service yard on the north side are 2.5 m below the level of the offices and main entrance. To the south of the test station a large winter garden contains a restaurant and library to provide a stimulating environment for informal meetings.

Office bays

Each wing of offices consists of five Miesian-inspired modules, based on Hopkins' own design for the Patera system (see Brookes, *Concepts in Cladding*, p. 90) divided by inset entrances. Each of the five modules is made up of five bays, with external Pratt roof trusses spanning 13.2 m from which the roof is hung, pinned to hollow section steel columns at 3.6 m centres, forming a hybrid portal frame (Figure 25.4). The method of waterproofing the structure as it punctures the roof covering is attained using a split collar slipped over the hangers during the erection of the frame and welded together and sealed around the hanger after the roof member has been laid (Figure 25.6).

The front facades of the offices are composed of double-glazed and laminated 3 m high aluminium sliding glazed units (Figure 25.5) with polyester powder-coated frames. Imported from West Germany, new extrusions

25.1.

25.1.
General view from south-west

25.2.
East–west section. 1 Drilling test station; 2 offices; 3 services undercroft

25.3.
Plan. 1 Main entrance; 2 reception; 3 winter garden; 4 drilling test station; 5 offices/ laboratories

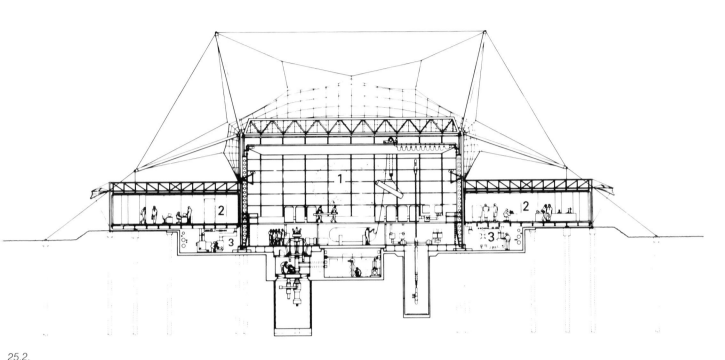

25.2.

were required to carry the weight of the glass. The ends of the long modules are clad with Plannja insulated profiled steel panels. Cold-rolled purlins 114 mm deep at 1.2 m centres support the 25 mm galvanized steel diaphragm roof, with a single-layer polymeric roof membrane laid to fall, with flashings and upstand (Figure 25.7).

The floor is galvanized steel decking, with 60 mm 'Styrofoam' insulation sandwiched between two layers of chipboard supported by 254 mm deep secondary beams at 1.2 m centres, on 406 mm deep rolled-section I-beams on the primary grid (Figure 25.8). Apart from the foundation slab, the entire system is dry assembly using prefabricated components. Lightweight demountable partitions by Classtech Ltd separate the office units. The internal glass walls are made of 21 mm thick laminated glass, acoustically sealed to protect office/laboratory accommodation from test-rig noise.

Structure

The roof membrane is attached to cables supported by an external steel framework based on a series of tubular lattice towers (2.4 m wide and 19.2 m apart) linked by prismatic beams (1.5 m deep spanning 24 m) with raking aerial booms connected by tension rods (Figure 25.9). The four-pinned portal formed by the main girder and beams is braced by triangular lattices positioned between the office units and braced in the other direction by ties between all main frames.

Throughout the courtyard structure, tie members have been used consisting of solid rods with threaded couplers and turnbuckles to allow adjustment of the ties. This number of threaded connections within a member must lead to a reduced factor of safety when compared with a more conventional welded solution. Due to this factor, and the critical nature of the tie elements, all ties which could cause collapse in the event of a failure have been duplicated and designed so that any one tie could support the working load of the building. The most detrimental effect of a tie failing would therefore be an increase in frame movements. Piled foundations of 450 mm diameter transmit high loads from eight double masts.

Membrane

Manufactured by the West German firm Stromeyer-

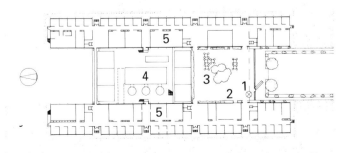

25.3

25.4.
Structural frame of offices. 1 Pratt truss: top boom 114.3 mm × 5 mm c.h.s., bottom boom 76.1 mm × 4 mm c.h.s.; 2 139.7 × 8 mm c.h.s. columns; 3 406 × 178 × 74 kg/m UB primary beam; 4 254 × 146 × 31 kg/m UB perimeter beam; 5 double glazing, 24 mm thickness overall, 6 mm toughened clear glass; 6 21 mm laminated clear glass; 7

services undercroft; 8 polyester powder-coated extruded aluminium louvres; 9 horizontal truss to brace main structural frame

25.5.
Glazed elevation to offices

25.6.
Detail of polymeric skirt flashing at joint between hangar and roof decking. 1 Bottom boom of truss; 2 hangar; 3 polymeric skirt flashing with stainless steel pipe clip (flashing bonded to polymeric roof membrane); 4 polystyrene insulation preformed to falls; 5 25 mm profiled steel decking; 6 galvanized 114 × 73 mm cold-formed steel purlins

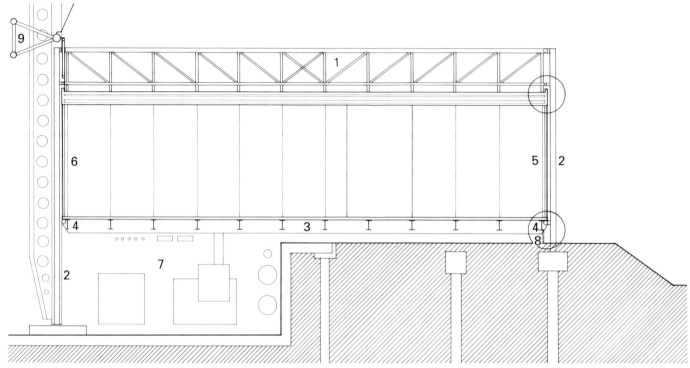

25.4.

25.5.

Ingenieurbau GmbH, the translucent Teflon-coated glassfibre membrane allows light into the testing areas. Because Teflon is an inert plastic, highly resistant to chemical attack and unaffected by ultraviolet light, it was claimed to offer a service life of more than 20 years with no discoloration with age (AJ, 24 October 1984, p. 4). The fabric is woven like cloth and the Teflon PTFE coating is applied by means of a dipping/sintering process.

A limitation in the width of the manufactured cloth has led to the membrane being constructed from a number of flat strips, the seams of which are lapped and heat welded in the factory. The edge of the fabric is then wrapped over a 20 mm galvanized steel strand cable (for a fuller description of this process see AJ, 24 October

25.7.
Office roof parapet detail. 1 Steel column 139.7 × 8 mm c.h.s.; 2 bottom boom of truss 114.3 × 5 mm c.h.s.; 3 preformed polymeric flashing fixed by steel clips; 4 single-layer 1 mm polymeric roof membrane over polystyrene insulation preformed to falls on 25 mm profiled steel decking; 5 extruded aluminium fascia panel; 6 galvanized steel 114 × 75 mm cold-formed purlin; 7 mineral fibre insulation 100 mm

thick suspended from decking; 8 continuous 100 × 75 mm steel glazing fixing angle attached to purlin hangar; 9 aluminium glazing frame; 10 24 mm thick overall double-glazing units; 11 perforated steel acoustic ceiling tiles

25.8.
Office floor/edge beam detail. 1 Aluminium glazing frame; 2 carpet on 22 mm T & G chipboard on 60 mm expanded polystyrene on chipboard; 3 perimeter fan-assisted convectors; 4 profiled galvanized steel decking; 5 edge beam 254 × 146 × 31 kg/m UB; 6 polyester powder-coated aluminium louvres; 7 galvanized steel primary beam 406 × 178 × 74 kg/m; 8 concrete blinding and kerb

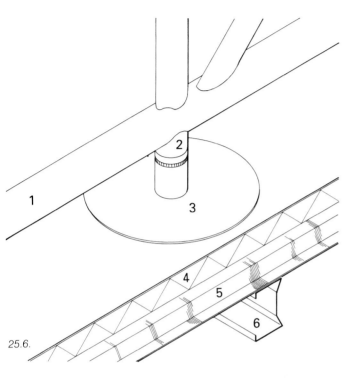

25.6.

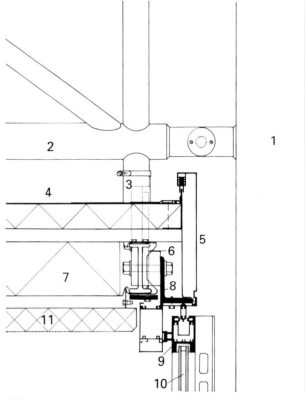

25.7.

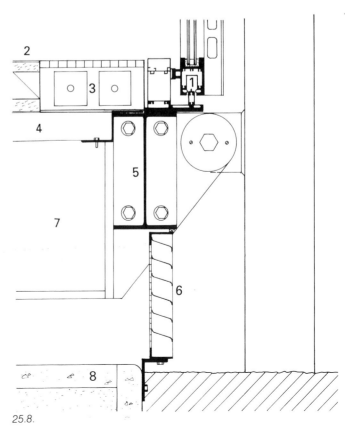

25.8.

1984, p. 54). The completed membrane is then transported to the site and clamped to the main structural cables, which evenly distribute the tension on the fabric when tightened.

The membrane's resistance to snow and wind loading and its double curvature were modelled on a computer by Arup Lightweight Structures Division. To fine tune the membrane once erected, its superstructure of masts, rods and cables incorporates adjustable pinned joints which also rotate according to changing live loads.

Services

The services for both laboratory/office units and the test-rig zone run below the floor level in undercrofts with

25.9.

access for maintenance. Heating is provided by a gas-fired boiler and a central chiller is located in the services compound. Offices are heated by fan-assisted perimeter convectors. The laboratories are air conditioned in the summer: extract grills are located in the floor and fumes are extracted and ducted to flue towers. The test-rig zone is partially heated. Electrical supply and data telecom cables run underfloor, rising to distribution points in the floor or office furniture. Cold water from the storage tank and hot water from the gas boiler are distributed via underfloor suspended piping: drainage is also suspended underfloor.

The tests rigs are isolated on resilient bearings to stop vibration transmission. Office/laboratory units are acoustically insulated with 21 mm laminated glazed wall and acoustic metal ceiling tiles.

Costs

Previously published articles indicate a cost of approximately £4 million, which suggests a building cost related to 5650 m^2 of offices and laboratories of approximately £675 per square metre after making allowance for external works. Of this figure, the work below the lowest floor finish accounts for nearly 20% of the building costs and the main frame, comprising eight double-masted tubular towers and the steel portal frames of the office blocks, 13%. The fabric roof and associated cables accounts for nearly 7%. Service costs are modest for a building of this type, mainly due to inexpensive heating and ventilation systems.

References

Architecture Aujourd'hui, No. 3237, February 1985, pp. LIX–LX,11–58 (English Summary pp. LII–LIV).

Architecture Movement Continuité, No. 9, October 1985, pp. 4–45. 'British Arch'.

A & U, No. 9 (192), September 1986, pp. 13–22.

Baumeister, **83**, No. 11, November 1986, pp. 34–39.

Croak, S., 'A Cambridge test: Hopkins for Schlumberger', *Architects' Journal*, **182**, No. 38, 18 September 1985, pp. 43–59.

Deutsche Bauzeitung, **120**, No. 2, February 1986, pp. 24–29.

Dietsch, D.K., 'Ties that bind', *Arch. Record*, **174**, No. 4, April 1986, pp. 136–147.

Hannay, P., 'A glimpse of tomorrow', *Architects' Journal*, **181**, No. 20, 15 May 1985, pp. 28–31.

Haward, B., 'Hopkins at Cambridge', *Architects' Journal*, **179**, No. 5, 1 February 1984, pp. 40–47.

Herzberg, H., 'High flyer', *Architects' Journal*, **180**, No. 43, 24 October 1984, pp. 43–63.

'Anthony Hunt: an architecturally minded builder', *Techniques & Arch.*, No. 356, October/November 1986, pp. 128–138.

Tubular Structures, No. 38, August 1985, pp. 16–17.

Sorting Office, Hemel Hempstead
Architects
Aldington, Craig & Collinge

General

Built in 1985 and situated on the St Albans Road/Park Lane junction in Hemel Hempstead (Figure 26.1), this sorting office was designed for the Eastern Postal Region by Aldington, Craig & Collinge and was required to house new sorting machines which were too large for the Post Office's existing buildings. The brief called for a general warehouse/industrial building with a 6 m minimum eaves height and no internal columns, with a high-level loading area on one side that would be marketable should the Post Office move out. The design takes advantage of the natural slope of the site to create a ground-floor public entrance below the sorting office on the south-west corner, which is linked to the administrative building by workshop areas. Although both main buildings are constructed using a light steel frame with a profiled steel composite cladding panel system on both walls and roof, it is the form of the sorting-office building which creates the most visual interest (Figure 26.2).

Structure

The structure of the sorting office consists of a series of 12 triangular cross-section lattice trusses made of tubular steel by Tubeworkers Ltd, spanning 28 m with a 12 m cantilever and overall depth of tubular truss of 1.5 m (Figure 26.3). Although at first sight these trusses and their steel cladding appear to wrap completely round the building on both sides, in reality they are propped on one side to allow a cantilevered overhang to the loading

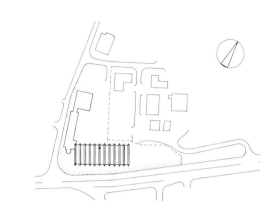

26.1. Site plan

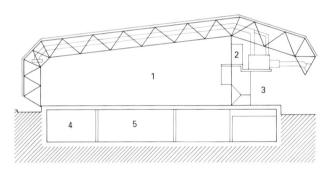

26.3.
Section through sorting office. 1 Sorting office; 2 watching gallery; 3 loading bay; 4 kitchen; 5 lounge/dining

26.2. General view from the south

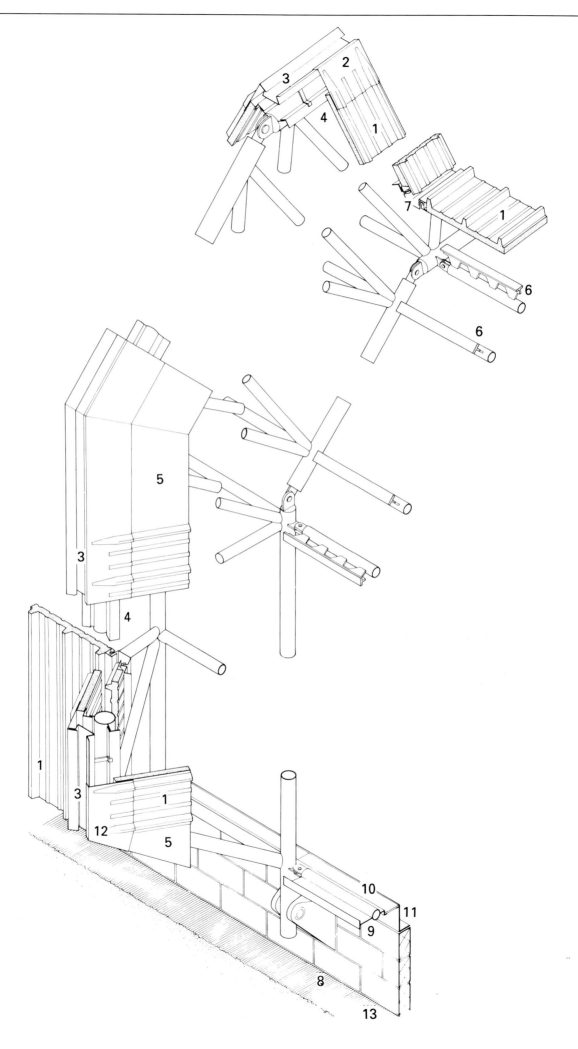

26.4.
Axonometric cutaway section through lattice truss and cladding. 1 Profiled Ondatherm panels; 2 standard pressed steel closer piece; 3 standard pressed steel gutter section supported on galvanized steel brackets; 4 steel fixing angles welded to c.h.s. at external apex of truss; 5 special insulated pressings used where cladding changes direction; 6 composite castellated purlin; 7 purpose-made extruded EPDM

gutter supported on 40 × 40 mm steel angles; 8 steel casting bolted to slab; 9 composite purlin; 10 rough-cast wired glass 6 mm thick; 11 200 × 100 mm steel angle kerbs bolted to blockwork; 12 special pressed steel closer piece; 13 fairface blockwork

26.5.
Profile of Ondatherm 101 composite panel

26.6.
Detail of Don Reynolds glazing mullion. 1 Extruded aluminium mullion; 2 press-fit gaskets; 3 glazing

areas. Trusses are stabilized horizontally by half-castellated I-beams welded to c.h.s. forming the purlins which are fixed to the lower chords of the truss (Figure 26.4). In addition, the paired vertical propping columns are also cross braced in their top section.

The method of fixing the base of the truss to the concrete below used a special iron casting cast by Exeter Casting Ltd and a stainless steel connector bolted to the concrete slab. The lightness of the structure is cleverly emphasized by an infill of rough-cast wired glass (6 mm thick) sitting on steel angles and silicone glazed.

The cladding

Both roofs and walls are clad with Ondatherm profiled double-skin steel composite panels (Figure 26.5) supplied by Azimex and fixed by Harold Shaw Contracts. In this case, the panels have a 50 mm polyurethane insulation core and have a smooth white Plastisol finish to the steel. They span between the purlins on the flat planes and on the projecting plane span in the opposite

direction between the chords of the trusses using steel fixing angles and flats, welded to the outer chord of the truss.

Where the panels change direction, pressed closer pieces are used to close off the section. These (or flashings) also occur at the projecting ends of the sheets. The architects, faced with the use of these standard elements, have cleverly used ridge and valley gutters to also allow each side of the truss to be expressed externally as separate planes and to permit changes of direction to occur in the flat parts of the sheet. It is this detail that makes this building so interesting for a student of cladding, in that such an elegant solution has been reached using standard parts. However, details of this type are susceptible to potential rain penetration unless the tolerances of assembly and the inherent movement/shrinkage of the EPDM gasket can be controlled.

The ridge gutter (coated steel pressing) is supported on galvanized steel brackets and the valley gutters are specially formed in extruded EPDM with moulded corners tucked into the metal pressings forming the ends of the Ondatherm panels. The EPDM gutter was made up and welded together in the factory, brought to site and fitted as one continuous run.

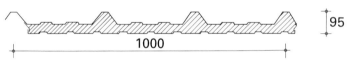

95
1000

26.5.

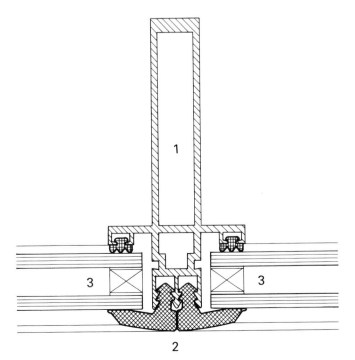

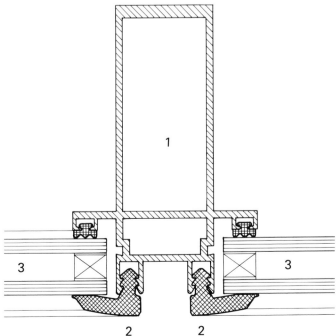

26.6.

26.7.

All roof rainwater is brought to ground level and collected in a continuous grill-covered ground gutter. In time there is some danger of the white cladding becoming streaked by the dirt in the rainwater, and it will probably need constant cleaning to maintain a pristine look.

Glazing

The west wall of the sorting office is clad in Don Reynolds double-glazed curtain walling composed of a polyester powder-coated extruded aluminium carrier system. This uses a split-section extrusion with a silicone glazing gasket (Figure 26.6).

Because of the height of the assembly (above 6 m), each of the curtain wall mullions is braced at its upper end by a triangulated c.h.s. frame descending diagonally from the outermost chord of the truss above, thus reducing the span of the transoms. The glazing supports are tied together at their base by stainless steel tie rods (Figure 26.7). Glazing is 24 mm double-glazed units formed in low E-glass inner leaf with tinted solar control glass outer leaf.

Services

The large plant required for heating the volume of air needed is situated outside, above the ancillary spaces and protected from the weather by the overhanging roof at the loading bays from which the ducts feed through the triangulated trusses. This allows easy access for maintenance without disrupting the sorting office, and is an excellent example of the integration between services and structure.

Costs

The building cost was £2.5 million, which, based on a total floor area, gives a cost per square metre of £424. Of this, the structural frame cost was £52 per square metre, the composite cladding forming the skin of the sorting office, inclusive of the gutter detail, cost £80 per square metre, while in the administration building the simpler roofscape cost £54 per square metre. The double-glazed aluminium curtain wall was approximately £200 per square metre. Thus the structural elements and shell of the building account for almost 50% of the building cost. However, the service elements are relatively inexpensive, being approximately 20% of the total cost, which compares well with other buildings of the same type.

Reference

Winter, J., 'Modern post architecture', *Architects' Journal*, 14 May 1986, pp. 37–58.

Stansted Airport Terminal Building, Essex
Architects
Foster Associates

General

The design of the Stansted Airport terminal building has tried to rediscover the simplicity and clarity of use characterized by the general aviation terminals of the earliest flying era. All public facilities are provided on a single concourse floor with arrivals and departures facilities planned side by side. With all baggage-handling systems, engineering plant, servicing and storage confined to an undercroft level below, the design is able to give a compact and flexible building which reduces walking distances for passengers and enables them to move through the building on essentially linear routes (Figure 27.1).

Another important aspect which has influenced the design is its context. For planning reasons, it was considered important that the building should not appear intrusive in the generally rural landscape of the locality. To this end, the undercroft has been partially excavated into the side of an existing rise in the ground, thereby establishing the concourse as an extension of ground level (Figure 27.2). The supports for the roof rise to 12 m at eaves level above the concourse, a height consistent

with existing mature trees in the surrounding landscape (Figure 27.3).

The form and external appearance of the terminal are designed to have an assertive and low profile, but at the same time to manifest a strong and recognizable presence. The two main elevations are fully glazed. External structural elements support 18 m deep canopies, which provide sun shading and eliminate strong reflections in the glass walls, making them transparent rather than reflective. The two side elevations are constructed from translucent white glass and pale silver-grey aluminium panels for the undercroft, with a low horizontal band of transparent glazing separating the two at concourse level (Figure 27.4).

To allow the airport a high degree of flexibility for future alterations and modifications, a 36 m structural bay has been generated. All distribution equipment for heating, ventilation, air conditioning and lighting serving the concourse is contained within the clusters of steel columns on this grid (Figure 27.5). A secondary 1.2 m planning grid supports free-standing enclosures for shops, kitchens, lavatories, etc., and these can be easily dismantled (Figure 27.6). These enclosures are 3.5 m

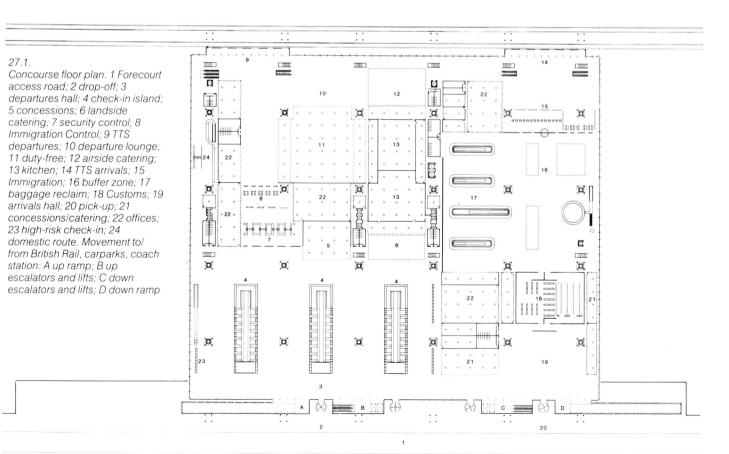

27.1.
Concourse floor plan. 1 Forecourt access road; 2 drop-off; 3 departures hall; 4 check-in island; 5 concessions; 6 landside catering; 7 security control; 8 Immigration Control; 9 TTS departures; 10 departure lounge; 11 duty-free; 12 airside catering; 13 kitchen; 14 TTS arrivals; 15 Immigration; 16 buffer zone; 17 baggage reclaim; 18 Customs; 19 arrivals hall; 20 pick-up; 21 concessions/catering; 22 offices; 23 high-risk check-in; 24 domestic route. Movement to/from British Rail, carparks, coach station: A up ramp; B up escalators and lifts; C down escalators and lifts; D down ramp

27.2.
*Diagrammatic north–south
section through terminal*

27.3.
*Photomontage of terminal set in
landscape*

27.4.
*Corner view of model showing
rapid transit system*

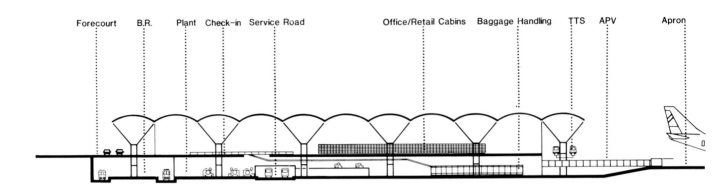

Forecourt   B.R.   Plant   Check-in   Service Road   Office/Retail Cabins   Baggage Handling   TTS   APV   Apron

27.2.

high and are serviced by independent environmental engineering systems located in the undercroft.

Structure

The steel roof consists of 121 low-rise tubular section lattice shells, supported by 36 pre-stressed 'trees'. These trees are 21 m tall and are spaced at 36 m centres. The 'trunks' of the trees consist of a cluster of four vertical 457 mm diameter tubes. These are joined by 355 mm diameter horizontal tubes forming a three-dimensional Vierendeel structure cantilevered off of concrete foundation pads. At the 13 m level (4 m above concourse level) the vertical members reduce in size and are articulated diagonally outwards from pinned connection points. These elements now form the 'branches' of the trees, whose tips are at the corner of an 18 m square. The upside-down truncated pyramid shape thus formed is cross braced internally by a three-dimensional arrangement of four 163 m diameter tubes and pairs of 40 mm diameter high-strength pre-stressing rods. During construction this bracing is jacked taut by a force of about 70 tonnes. It is this pre-stressing which allows all the structural elements to be reduced to minimal sectional sizes.

Although these elements are principally fabricated, all primary node assembly components take the form of high-strength steel castings ranging in size from 25 to over 500 kg. In particular, this method of production has enabled the realization of the complex conical branch tapered sections. All castings have been designed to meet North sea oil-rig material performance standards and have been mechanically tested at the National Engineering laboratories in Scotland (Figure 27.7).

In fabrication, two types of welding process have been employed: first, submerged-arc automatic welding for all large-section tubular butt welds; and second, manually injected gas welding for small-section tubes and attachments. The selection and application of weld types have been carefully considered in accordance with overall structural hierarchy and fabrication requirements.

The configuration of trees and shells has the advantage that, while the passenger concourse is interrupted by structure only every 36 m, the roof panels themselves have to span only 18 m (Figure 27.8). Both dimensional systems respond respectively to the integrated requirements of planning at floor level and of lighting and

27.3.

27.4.

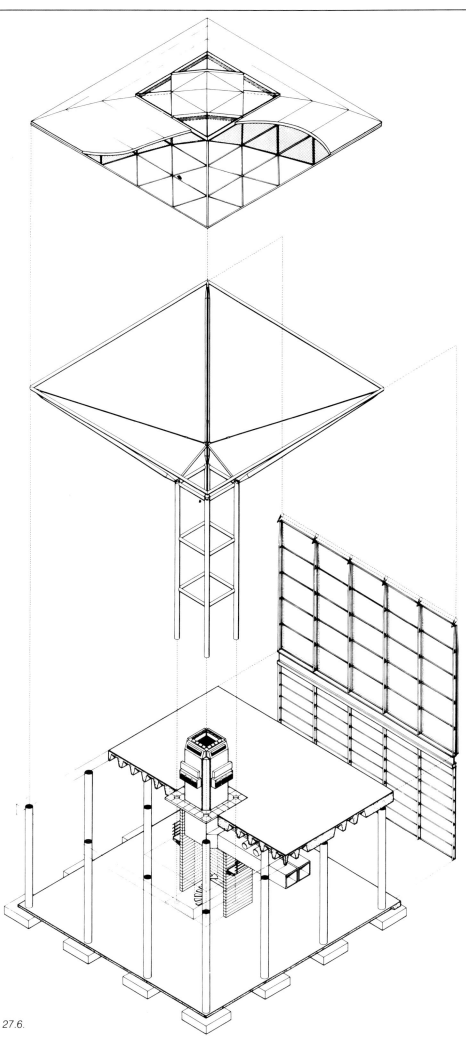

27.6.
Exploded isometric of cabin
structure and services

27.6.

103

27.5.
*Exploded isometric of structural
tree and services*

acoustical behaviour at ceiling level. Additionally, the 2.5 m high lattice shells have been sized for constructability, since each is assembled fully on the ground, including profiled aluminium decking, and lifted directly onto the top of each tree and sets of interconnecting gridline beams by a large crawler crane (Figure 27.9). Similarly, the Vierendeel trunk structures are also fabricated entirely off-site and lifted into position as complete elements. Overall, the structural steelwork has been designed to minimize the amount of on-site assembly.

Another particularly unique feature of the structure is that, over its entire 198 × 198 m plan area, it possesses no expansion joints. Some slight rotational bending movement around gridline beam splice locations is allowed for, and this lets the structure react to wind and live loading without distortion. The gridline beam connection to the top of tubular steel wall cladding mullions allows for dynamic and thermal differential movement to occur. The decision to avoid expansion joints in the steelwork meant that they could also be avoided in the roof plane, thereby greatly simplifying the details.

Finally, the entire structure will be painted in a specially developed Isocyanate modified urethane acrylic decorative system, which allows for particularly fine colour

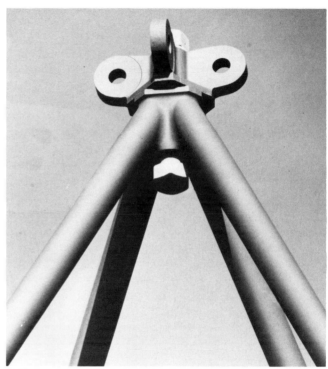

27.7.

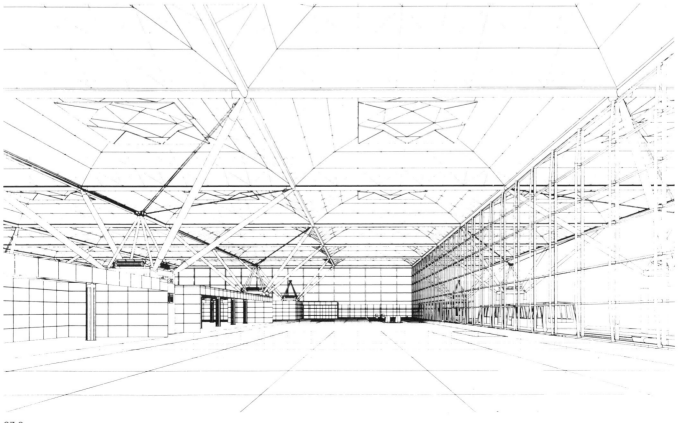

27.8.

27.9.
*Lattice shell being lifted onto
gridline beams*

27.9.

balancing with the indirect artificial lighting system and also exhibits significantly improved resistance to chemical and solar attack.

The total weight of steel in the structure is about 2800 tonnes and 4 hectares of profiled aluminium decking, also within the steelwork contract, are being used. Welded to the steelwork are about 110 000 cleats, lugs and brackets for the later attachment of cladding and high-level services. The steelwork contract was executed by Tubeworkers Limited of Claverdon in Warwickshire. Fabrication commenced in late summer 1986 and erection started on-site in spring 1987.

References

Davey, P., 'Stansted Structure', *Architectural Review*, No. 1072, June 1986.

Papadakis, A.C., 'Foster Associates, London Stansted Airport Terminal, *Architectural Design*, No. 56, May 1986.

Vitta, M., 'Steel trees in nature', *L'Arca*, June 1986.

Waters, B., 'Screws, nuts and teapot castings', *Building*, 11 September 1987.

Swindon Leisure Centre
Architects
Borough of Thamesdown Architects' Department
Borough Architect K.P. Sherry

General

This leisure complex, comprising sporting and social facilities together with bars and cafés, is situated in the development area to the west of Swindon, very near Norman Foster's Renault Centre, both of which use masted structures (Figure 28.2). Built in 1984, the complex has an ice rink, a 25 m swimming pool, a sports hall, squash courts, a health suite, arts and drama studios, snooker rooms, a youth club, a library and administration. A central mall connecting a café/restaurant, bar and information centre is located in the heart of the scheme to provide access to all these functions. The initial concept was based on a major roof structure embracing all the accommodation. Most of the building is at ground and first-floor levels with a small second-floor area. The site slopes north to south by just under a storey height, which allows the entrance from the buses to be at first-floor level.

The building was constructed in a remarkably short time between June 1983 and April 1985, using a prefabricated structure specially designed by structural engineers Anthony Hunt Associates.

Structure

The structure consists of a primary two-way lattice of 2.5 m deep girders at 14.4 m centres spanning from columns 93.6 m apart. The centre of the structure is formed by a 9 m^2 tower which also accommodates most of the air-handling plant (Figure 28.1). From these masts and those at the perimeter tension cables are used to assist the span of the lattice. These are restrained over the tops of the perimeter columns via outriggers to the base of the assembly (Figure 28.2). A series of smaller girders within this grid support the profiled steel sheeting forming the roof deck. The roof perimeter is formed by a triangulated lattice girder giving edge stiffness which is expressed as a cornice to the building.

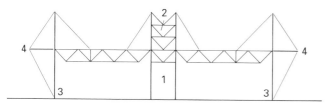

28.1.
Structural diagram. 1 Central tower; 2 services platform; 3 perimeter masts; 4 outrigger

28.2. *Side view showing masted structure*

Sequence of erection

The sequence of erection began from the central tower and progressed with each quarter of the roof completed in an anti-clockwise direction. (Was this because the crane driver was left-handed?) Stainless steel pins were used to connect the roof structure and nodes of the tension cables and the whole system was designed to maximize the number of repetitive elements to facilitate fabrication. An internal steel frame provides support for the precast concrete upper floors, and is fireclad where necessary and structurally independent of the main roof.

Cladding

This steel frame is also used to support the external cladding of profiled coated steel sheet and glazing. The cladding used is Glammett steel-faced foam-cored composite panels finished in silver PVF^2 and fixed by Metecno Contracts UK Ltd. Internal walls are generally fairfaced blockwork to supportspaces and public areas.

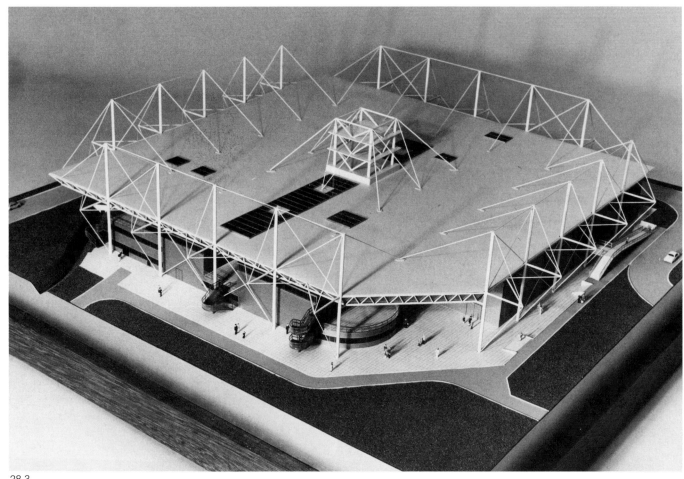

28.3.

Services

The building is mechanically ventilated with air conditioning limited to the sports areas. Heat for the whole building is generated from the rink refrigeration plant, backed up by gas-fired boilers. Electrical services incorporate a BMS system for computer control and logging of all plant, and this level of sophistication is reflected in other systems of fire detection, security, public address and lighting.

Costs and comments

With a roofed area of 8760 m² and an internal floor area (including the two-storey block) of 12 500 m², the building cost of £9 million represents £720 per square metre, which, for a building of this type, is a reasonably low-cost budget. Considerable innovation in the design and the attention to the form of the structural components and their expression make this building worth further study. For instance, the design of the canopies over the main entrances in simple frame and profiled cladding construction fit easily within the general sense of the building construction.

References

Anthony Hunt Associates, *Selected projects 1965–1985*, edited by Stratton and Reekie, produced in association with Book Production Consultants.

Ostler, T., 'The Swindon effect', *Building Design,* 17 October 1986, pp. 30–31.

The Trading Building, Haarlem
Architects
Cepezed

General

On an industrial estate near Haarlem, in Holland, this low-cost industrial unit with its highly visible mast structure is included here for its ingenious but simple use of components and the relationship between structure and cladding. It was built in 1985 by the architects Cepezed (Jan Pesman and Michel Cohen), and illustrates the architects' continuing search for the relationship between design and production, taking account of advances in fabrication techniques. This approach is illustrated by previous designs by the same architects, such as the refurbishment system for PTT (*Architectural Review*, February 1985) and their Heiwo-House. These designs and others yielded much information about the use of self-supporting sandwich panels, which was subsequently employed in the Trading Building, Haarlem, and its successors. The designers admit, therefore, that this building is a prototype, and although there may be some criticism of its architectural form, the simplicity of detailing resulting in a low-cost assembly should be admired.

Structure

The sixteen 5 m wide bays of structure comprise 17 sets of pylons positioned centrally along the 30 m wide rectangle (Figure 29.1), supporting, by cables, cantile-

29.2.

29.3.

29.1.
Section

29.2.
Boom pinned to 100 mm c.h.s.

29.3.
100 mm c.h.s. pinned to concrete slab

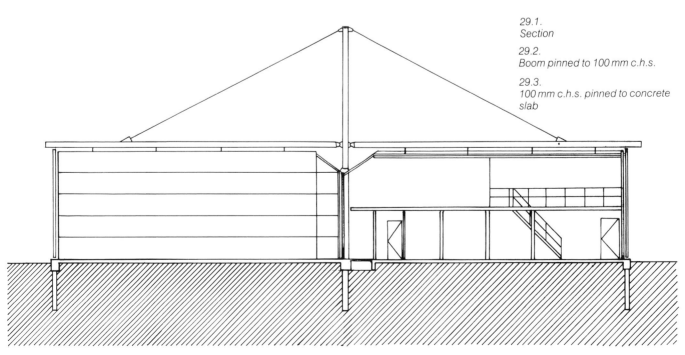

29.1.

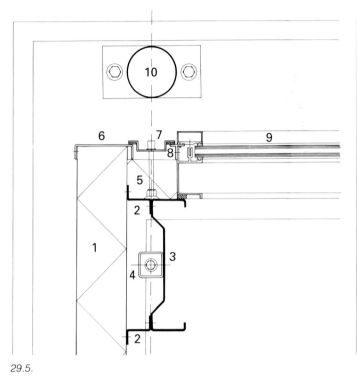

29.5.

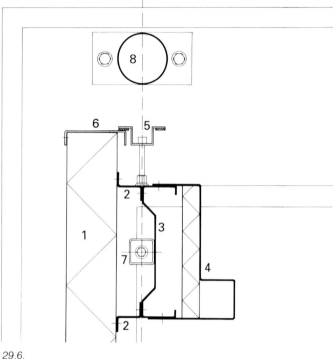

29.6.

vered booms each spanning 15 m. These booms (355 mm diameter c.h.s.) are tied at their ends to the ground slab by 100 mm diameter c.h.s. pinned at their bases (see Figures 29.2 and 29.3). Cross bracing is provided within each bay of the masts and outriggers are included at the ends.

Cladding

The cladding is composed of a 100 mm sandwich panel of two skins of 0.6 mm steel laminated to a polystyrene insulation, and the 15 m side panels are unusually long

29.4.

(Figure 29.4) with interim supports at 5 m centres. The panel skins have been roll formed from 1200 mm wide coil resulting in panels 1155 mm wide. The panels are supported by vertical multi-beams, which are in turn fixed at their head to 100 × 100 mm r.h.s. suspended from the structural booms.

The panels are fixed to the structure by means of pressed steel cleats and the doors and windows are directly attached to the vertical multi-beam (Figures 29.5 and 29.6). The 102 mm vertical joints between the panels and windows consist of site-applied insulation and a top-hat section, painted to match the panels, which is screwed back into a nut welded to the multi-beam. The accuracy in placing these multi-beams is therefore very critical.

An interesting feature of this jointing assembly is the T-shaped adaptor to the windows to form a back plate against which the top-hat cover piece can be sealed. Similarly, the ends of the panels are capped in a aluminium U-section which is oversized on one side to allow a bearing plate for the top-hat cover piece. The same section with the outer flange bent by 45 degrees is used as a capping to the eaves detail (Figure 29.7).

Horizontal joints between the panel are tongue and groove joints formed in the polystyrene insulation, with a face-sealed silicone joint. At the base of the panel (Figure 29.8) an Omega 25 × 25 mm profile allows a similar upstand detail, also acting as a location slot.

29.7.
*Eaves detail. 1 Sandwich panel; 2
30 × 116 × 3 mm aluminium
channel; 3 hanger; 4 100 × 100 ×
4 mm r.h.s.; 5 106 mm deep
profile roof deck; 6 355 mm
diameter c.h.s. boom*

29.8.
*Detail at base of cladding. 1
Sandwich panel; 2 25 × 25 mm
'Omega' profile channel; 3
concrete slab*

29.9.
*Detail at skylight. 1 100 × 100 ×
4 mm r.h.s.; 2 106 mm deep
profile roof deck; 3 pressed metal
edging; 4 'Skylight' glazing
system*

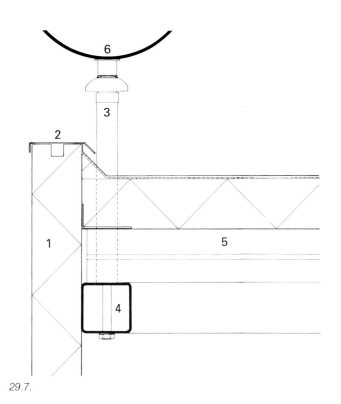

29.7.

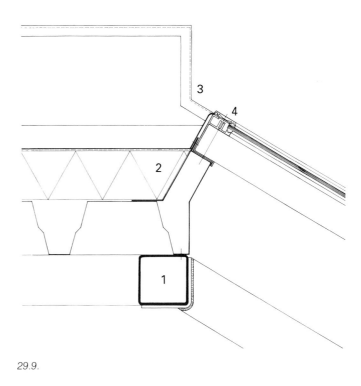

29.9.

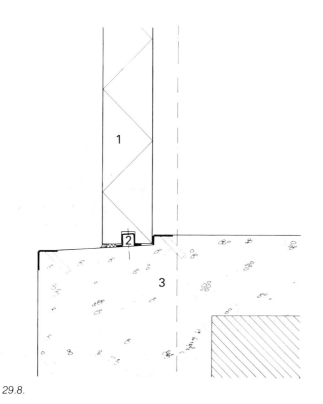

29.8.

Roofing

The 106 mm deep profile roof deck is supported by 100 × 100 × 4 mm r.h.s. suspended from the main boom. This kind of penetration of the roof by the supporting framework can be difficult to waterproof (see Figure 29.7). (See, for example, case studies of the Patera System and IBM Sports Pavillion in Brookes, *Concepts in Cladding*.)

The metal decking is sealed to provide a vapour barrier, with 100 mm polystyrene insulation and PVC roof covering above. In the centre of the building a continuous skylight-glazing system is provided. The detail of the junction between the glazing and the underside of the roof deck using a metal flashing is shown in Figure 29.9.

References

Berni, L. and Leyroy, A., 'Holland: a constructive work-shop', *Ottagono*, No. 84, p. 23.

Mass, T., 'High-tech: het controleerbare beelt', *Architectur – Bouwen*, February 1987, pp. 23–26.

Van Douwen, A.A., 'Bedrijfsgebouewen in Nederland', Staaldocumentatie No. 1, *Bijlage Gebouwen met staal*, No. 81, June 1987.

30

'Yacht House' System, Woodgreen
Architect
Richard Horden Associates

General

Considering Richard Horden's previous experience with Foster Associates on the Sainsbury Centre and his enthusiasm for small boats, it is perhaps not altogether surprising that he should have been involved in the design of the 'Yacht House' modular frame building system in conjunction with Proctor Masts (manufacturers), Anthony Hunt (engineer) and the Scott Sutherland School of Architecture (development). As a prototype for a range of designs using the same structural system, Horden built a house at Woodgreen, in the New Forest, Hampshire, for his sister. Using entirely self-build parts (apart from the ground slab and drainage systems), the house was finally completed in 1985 at a price of around £300 per square metre, although Horden claimed a saving of £30 000 overall using self-build construction methods.

The house plan consists of a rectangle, four bays ×

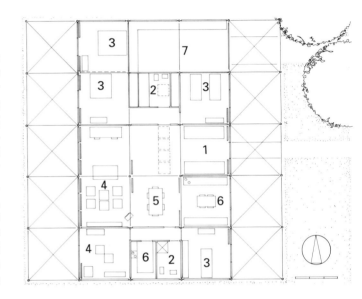

30.1.

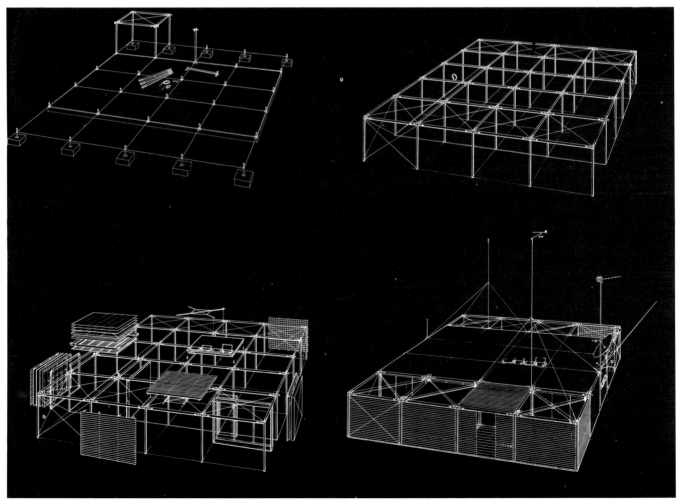

30.2–5.

30.1
Plan: the bays on the south side
form a granny flat. 1 Entrance hall;
2 bathroom; 3 bedroom; 4 living
room; 5 dining room; 6 kitchen; 7
garage

30.2.
Assembly sequence. Setting out
and pouring of concrete pad
foundations and ground slab.
Columns and spars erected with
wind bracing

30.3.
Wind-frame complete. Two
opposite corners have vertical
wind bracing to ensure rigidity in
the vertical plane

30.4.
Cladding and roof panels added

30.5.
The completed house

30.6.
Section through column head
detail. 1 Aluminium spar with
cutouts; 2 cruciform aluminium
member made up from 400 × 100
× 12mm; 3 76mm diameter
aluminium column; 4 50 × 100 ×
10mm × 80mm long aluminium
angle to take roof panel frame

30.7.
Part plan, part section of column
head. 1 Aluminium spar with
cutouts; 2 cruciform aluminium
member made up from 400 × 100
× 12mm plate; 3 76mm diameter
aluminium column; 4 bolts with
spacers welded to cruciform
plate; 5 50 × 100 × 10mm ×
80mm long aluminium angles

five bays, with a 3.6m grid to give a variety of living spaces with partitions and using yacht masts as aluminium structural columns on the same grid (Figure 30.1). An interesting aspect of the plan is the variety of inside/outside spaces. Interior modules are covered by solid roof panel comprising metal decking and insulation held down to the deck by marine plywood sheets and all supported by steel angle trays. Some areas such as terraces and garage are covered by fabric canopies, roller reefed to control shading. Other external areas are defined by white variable-pitch aluminium louvres, below which is positioned the cross bracing for wind resistance.

The principle of construction and sequence of assembly (Figures 30.2–30.5), starting with the assembly of columns (masts) and beams (spars) and wind bracing, prior to letting in the roof panels each framed in a steel angle, illustrates Horden's intention to use the elements of yacht technology to produce an interchangeable arrangement of parts which can be easily assembled with unskilled labour – 'like a windsurfing kit for the building industry'.

Structure

The structure is composed of a series of extruded aluminium masts at 3.6m intervals connected by extruded aluminium spars which form a permanent grid into which a variety of roof and wall panels can be placed. At Woodgreen the roof panels are metal decking, insulation and plywood mounted within a steel frame, but other later developments include g.r.p. panels.

To some extent, the aluminium spars can be considered to be redundant once the roof panels are in place, as these then serve to transfer the load to the aluminium masts. Certainly, the spars then serve no structural purpose (see Winter). However, if the masts can be seen to be permanent bracing to ease the erection process

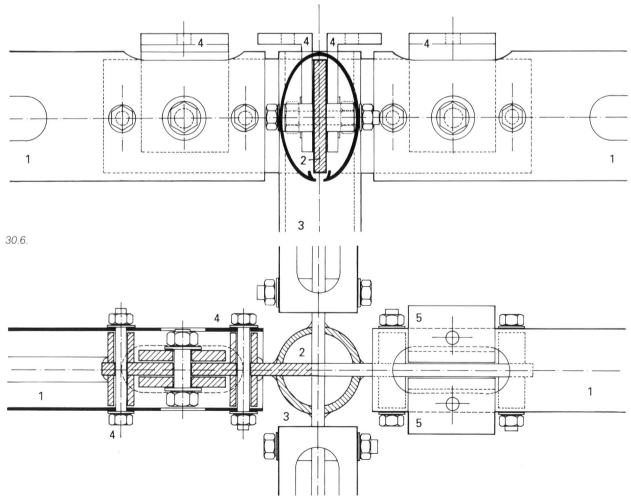

30.6.

30.7.

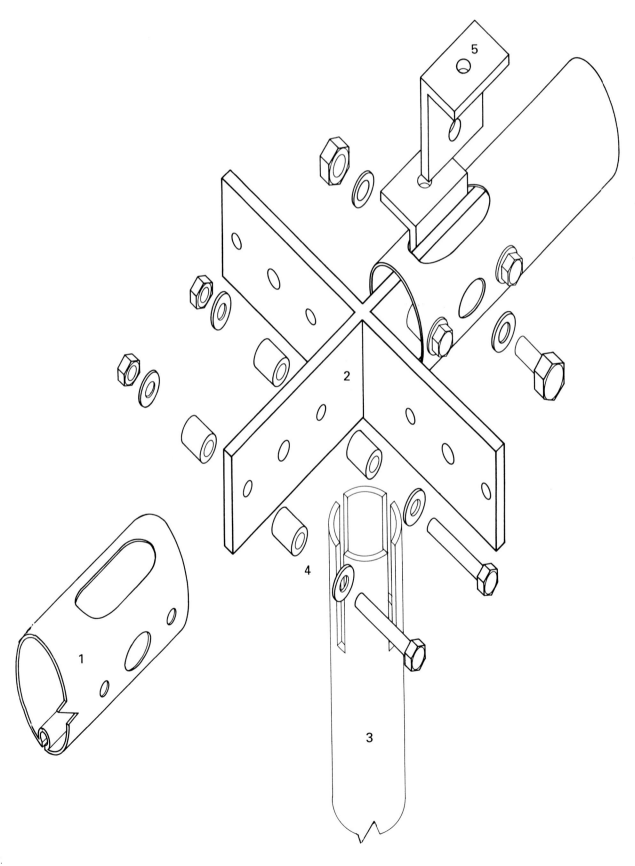

30.8.
Axonometric of column head
assembly. 1 Aluminium spar with
cutouts; 2 cruciform aluminium
member made up from 400 × 100
× 12 mm plate; 3 76 mm diameter
aluminium column; 4 bolts with
spacers welded to cruciform
plate; 5 50 × 100 × 10 mm ×
80 mm long aluminium angles

30.8.

30.9.
Column head assembly showing
roof panel frames resting on
aluminium angles

30.10.
External corner showing spars
fixed to column with aluminium
louvre panel

30.11.
Horizontal section through
column and patio door jamb. 1
76 mm diameter aluminium
column; 2 76 × 76 × 5 mm
aluminium angle; 3 door jamb

30.9.

30.10.

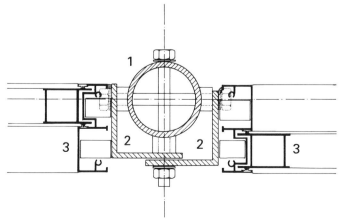

30.11.

and allow interchangeability to the parts, then they are an integral part of the total system. In the house at Woodgreen the spars, painted white and exposed wherever possible, do perform a visual function and can also be used to distribute services through their hollow section.

The details (Figures 30.6–30.8) show the 76 mm diameter × 6 mm thick extruded aluminium mast slotted at its head to receive a stainless steel cross plate 400 mm wide which extends down the hollow centres of the oval-shaped aluminium spars. These are each then fixed with two stainless steel bolts with short stainless spacer tubes welded to the cross plate so that the bolts do not squeeze the spar, and 50 × 100 × 80 mm aluminium angles × 10 mm thick are then also bolted either side of the cross plates and project through pre-cut slots in the top of the spars. These then support the steel angle framing the roof panels (Figure 30.9).

Cladding

The exterior of the house is clad with white aluminium weatherboarding on the sides, mounted onto a cladding unit 3572 mm long × 2400 mm high (Figure 30.10). The front and back elevations have sliding patio doors extending the full 2.4 m floor-to-ceiling dimensions. These glazed doors are fixed to the aluminium tubular masts using 76 × 76 × 6 mm steel angles (Figure 30.11).

Although the house can be admired as an example of clip-together detailing, some of this seems a little crude in comparison to what might have been possible in boat design. To some extent this can be explained by the requirement to self-build, and must have been affected by the cost of the component parts, aluminium masts, stainless steel plates, etc. Even so, it does represent an elegant example of interchangeable component assembly, and with its extensive use of adjustable louvres can be compared to Chris Clarke's Bridge House in Brisbane (Case Study 5). Both architects would have been influenced by Craig Elwood and the Mies tradition.

References

Anon., 'Yacht haven', *Building Design Practice Profile*, 15 March 1985.

Horden, R., 'Yacht-House', *Architecture d'Aujourd'hui*, No. 239, June 1985, pp. 1–47.

Winter, J., 'Ship to shore', *Architects' Journal*, 24 July 1985, pp. 36–50.

Victoria Plaza Canopy, London
Architects
Heery Architects & Engineers Ltd

General

When commissioned by Salomon Brothers International Ltd to transform an existing atrium into a dealing room Heery Architects & Engineers Ltd, together with Anthony Hunt Associates, were faced with an unusual problem. The solution was to insert a suspended services canopy which would control the environment below, transforming it from a dead space into the nerve-centre for the whole building. This new roof thus divides the height of the atrium the top of which can be seen from the two floors of offices above.

The 30 × 40 m atrium was ringed by four levels of office space and split down the centre by a two-storey high link block. The whole office block had been constructed above the railway tracks at Victoria Station and consequently the loading points were severely restricted. The brief requirements also added further complexity to the project: the client stated that the dealing room had to be operational by the 'Big Bang' in 1986, only 14 months away when Heery were commissioned. Second, the structure to be inserted was to be fully demountable, since the building would have to be reinstated when Salomon's lease ran out.

Structure

By removing the link block the atrium became one uninterrupted space. This also freed the building of 134 tonnes, which dictated the limits within which the new structure had to lie (Figure 31.1). The side walls of the atrium had not been designed to carry any further load and could not be used for support.

Having established the three loading points, the design was originally based on one mast rising off each

31.2.

of these points from which a Vierendeel box truss (fabricated by Tubeworkers Ltd) could be suspended. Each span is picked up by three pairs of 40 mm diameter rods (maximum load in hangers 105 kN) (Figure 31.2). Since the mast location was offset by 3 m from the centre of the span, counterweights equivalent to the weight of the structure plus services of one bay had to be added to the shorter bay to balance out the loads. When, at a later date, in an attempt to reduce the number of visual obstructions in the dealing room one of the (273 mm diameter, 16 mm wall thickness) columns was eliminated the geometry of the suspension rods increased in complexity, since a total of 48 rods had to be anchored to two column heads (Figure 31.3).

The top level of the canopy plane was set by the office floor level and the structural depth of the Vierendeel box truss was coordinated with the 900 mm depth of the

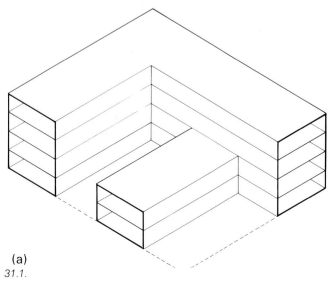

(a)
31.1.

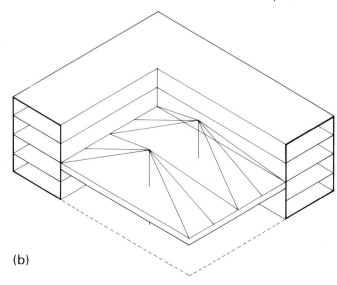

(b)

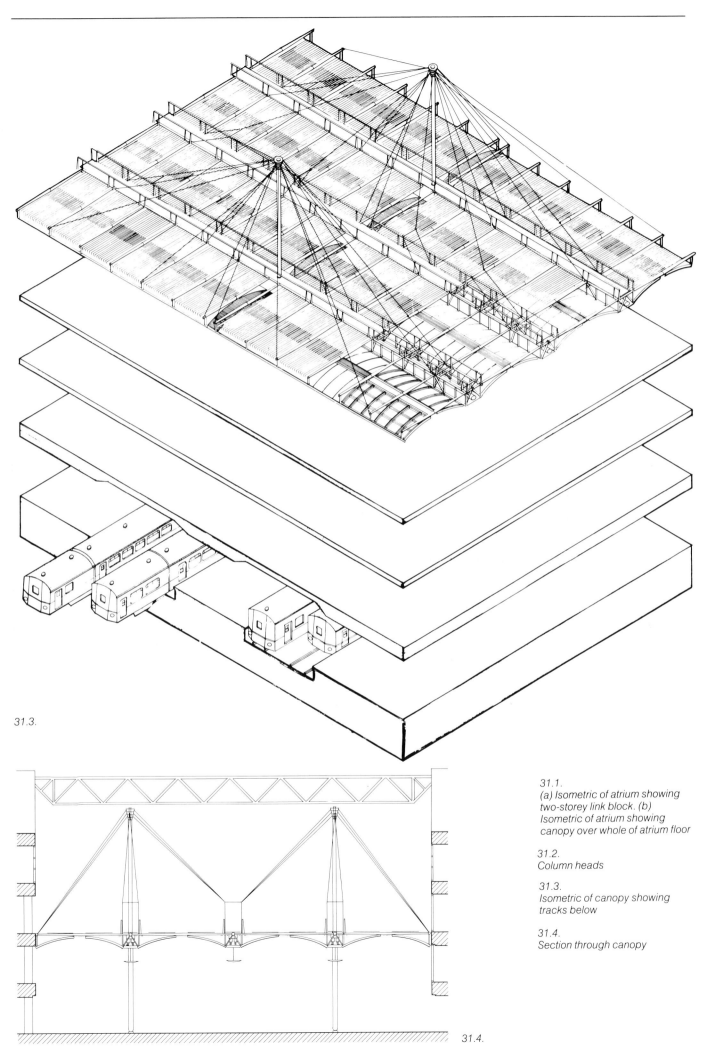

31.3.

31.4.

31.1.
(a) Isometric of atrium showing
two-storey link block. (b)
Isometric of atrium showing
canopy over whole of atrium floor

31.2.
Column heads

31.3.
Isometric of canopy showing
tracks below

31.4.
Section through canopy

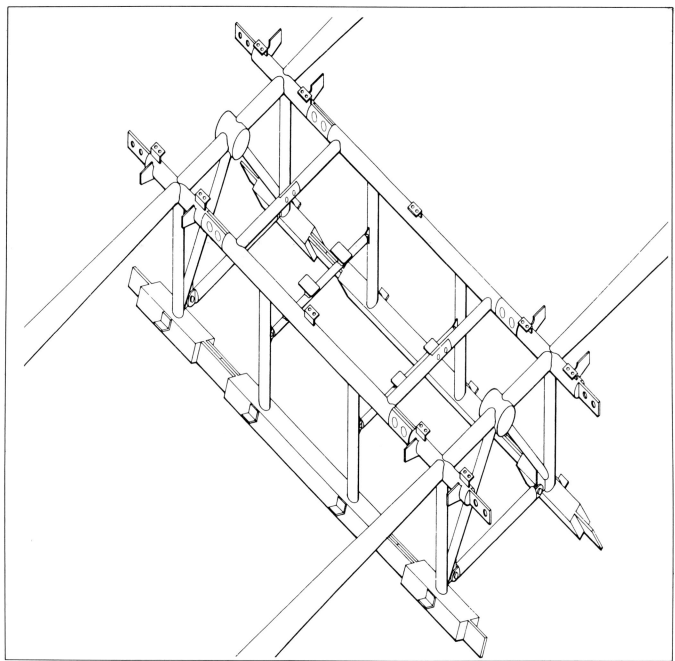

31.5.

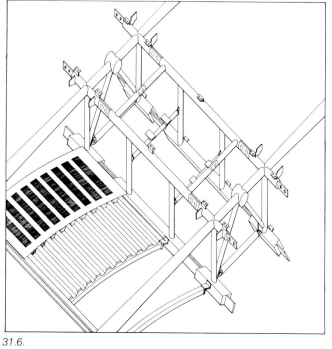

31.6.

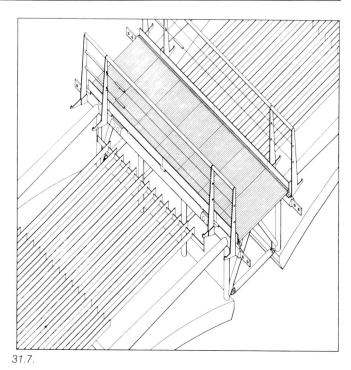

31.7.

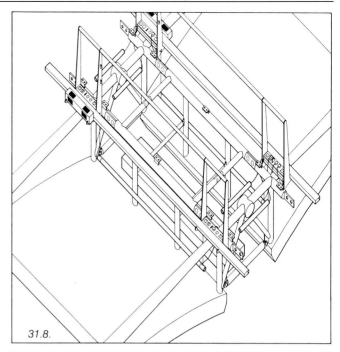

31.8.

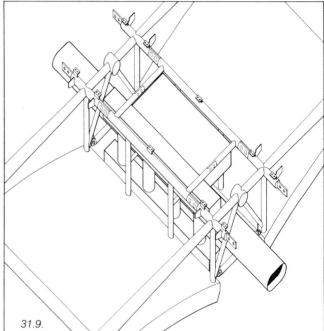

31.9.

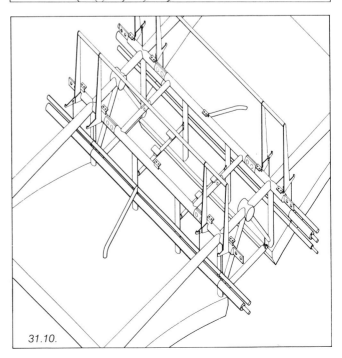

31.10.

cladding spandrel. In this way the canopy does not impinge on the glazed areas of the surrounding offices (Figure 31.4). The maximum depth of structure is required along the box truss 'spines'. The vaulted ceiling rises where this depth is not required, at the same time adding to the visual interest and improving the acoustic qualities of the space below. The 6.3 m long members spanning from spine to spine were designed as double-tapered 'cigar'-shaped circular hollow sections, which makes optimum use of material where the bending moments are greatest . Unfortunately, these had to be abandoned after prototyping led to programming difficulties.

Erection of the canopy within an existing building meant that the size of each component was limited to the physical limits of the access to the site, which was a 1.2 × 3.6 m opening in the cladding, and the weight of each component was limited to that which could be manhandled by a small team of erectors. These constraints dictated that the canopy had to be made up of many small elements. A family of in-line connections was derived to reduce the number of joints which may otherwise have been visually dominant (Figure 31.5). The Vierendeel construction also helped in this respect, since a triangulated truss would also have required joints in the diagonal members.

Diagonal bracing was achieved in the plane of the canopy by using profiled steel panels which were fixed to the secondary steelwork (Figure 31.6) to provide a stressed-skin construction. The requirement for diagonal bracing in an internal structure is minimal, and was quite simply and unobtrusively dealt with.

Due to the severe loading restrictions the weight of the structure had to be kept to a minimum. This meant that much of the tertiary structure (handrails and stanchions, walkways and kickplates) and services (fan coil casings, cable trunking, pipe casings and light fittings) were made of aluminium (Figure 31.7).

Because of the requirement to fully demount the structure at some future date the columns are not anchored at their base. Instead they sit into a pocket at their base and are restrained by the tension structure above (Figure 31.12).

Services

All services enter the canopy from the end of each spine and run towards the columns, terminating in the central bays, leaving a clear slot running across the canopy along the column line. Each 3 m bay is subdivided into 500 mm wide units, which provides a framework for the coordination of services (Figures 31.8–31.10). The ser-

31.11.
General view: note in-line
connectors on structural
members and ball and socket
joint on top half of column

31.11.

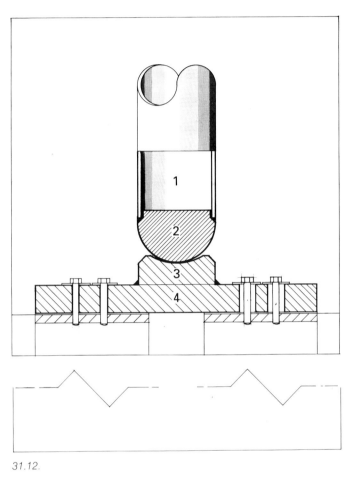

31.12.
Detail of column base. 1 273 mm
diameter × 16 mm c.h.s.; 2
machined solid steel hemisphere
welded to column; 3 machined
solid steel cup to take column; 4
solid steel base plate spans
expansion joint

31.12.

vices include: air handling, above- and below-canopy lighting and associated ballast units, communications, pneumatics, sprinklers and general power. Each socket box is punched out with six different socket types giving each electrical service its own dedicated outlet. The below-canopy lighting consists of emergency lighting, uplighters and downlighters. The uplighters were specially designed to reflect light evenly off the vaulted ceiling, mixing halogen and sodium sources to create a different effect in the mornings and evenings. The downlighters were chosen from Siemens range specially developed to eliminate glare on VDU screens.

Acoustic control in a dealing room is potentially a great problem, but the use of perforated ceiling tiles with acoustic backing provided this. Acoustic insulation was also fitted in the troughs of the profiled steel sheet, which were then covered with perforated panels to provide insulation in the case of noise break-out in the canopy space above.

References

Knobel, L., 'Dealing with tradition', *Designers' Journal*, March 1987.
Latham, I., 'Over the top', *Building Design*, 22/29 August 1986.
Thornton, J., 'The lightweight canopy at Victoria Plaza', *Architectural Journal*, 29 October 1986.

Hongkong and Shanghai Bank, Hong Kong
Architects
Foster Associates

32.1.

General

This case study (Figure 32.1) has been included towards the conclusion to this book mainly because it represents the ultimate use of component technology applied to buildings produced to date. Each element of the construction was developed in conjunction with the manufacturers, with claddings from the USA, fire protection of the structure from the UK, staircases from Japan, external sunscoops from West Germany, inner sunscoops from Austria, floor finishes from Finland and refuse disposal from Sweden (Figure 32.2). Each element was designed and developed from scratch in collaboration with the manufacturers. Mock-ups and prototypes were built and tested until their performance and quality met with the architects' approval. In some respects therefore one could regard this building as the ultimate in custom-made component assembly.

One of the factors influencing the architects in their selection of manufacturers was their willingness and ability to manufacture non-standard items. This was

certainly the case in the design of the cladding and curtain wall system, by the cladding contractors Cupples and their parent company H.H. Robertson. The cladding contract for the bank not only represented the largest ever (45 million m^2) but also the most complex in its need to respond to the geometry of the structure and its tolerances, and also to be capable of resisting typhoon conditions.

Cladding panels

The first cladding panels were fitted to a section of the main structure on 23 January 1985 (Figure 32.3). Fire protection to the structure had been achieved using a thin, highly flexible ceramic fibre blanket by Morceau UK, held in position on a stainless steel mesh. A reinforced aluminium foil was wrapped over the completed fire protection to provide a vapour seal and temporary protection prior to fixing the cladding.

The aluminium cladding panels with their extruded edge sections were fixed back through the blanket using cleats onto Unistrut sections attached to the steel frame at the time of applying the 12 mm thick cementicious barrier coating, providing corrosion protection to the structural steelwork (Figure 32.4). Some of the 9 mm joints between the panels were filled with silicone mastic, others were pressure equalized.

Similar aluminium panels were used to clad both the inside and outside of the building. The service modules are also clad using honeycomb-cored aluminium panels. These were produced by Cupples, using purpose-made presses and specially developed robot welders using 4 mm thick plate aluminium with a Duranar PVF^2 finish to produce a large range of individual panels based on a 1200 mm grid. The largest panel covered the joint of the cantilevered truss and the outer hanger (Figure 32.5). Designed and tested to prevent water penetration even under typhoon conditions, great care had to be taken with all panels to ensure that they were located accurately and that all joints were correctly sealed. The weather protection of the complete assembly depends upon the principle of pressure equalization within the joint.

Curtain walling

The great depth of the Bank's offices and Foster's desire for a see-through building on two elevations dictated a fully glazed solution on the Queen's Road side of the elevations to Statue Square. Here the adoption of a curtain walling system spanning between floor levels consisted of a clear-glass outer skin, a cavity containing a venetian blind and an openable inner leaf of tinted

32.1.
General view of Bank in context

32.2.
Chart showing origin of
components

32.3.
First cladding panels to be
erected

32.3.

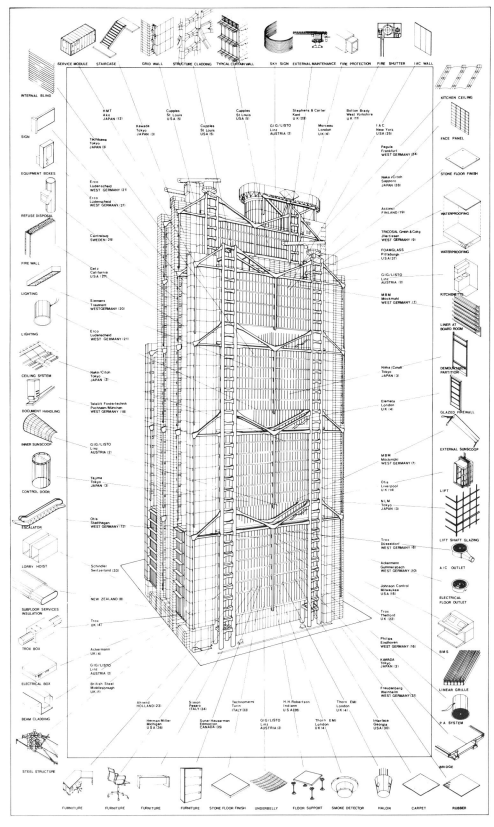

32.2.

SERVICE MODULE STAIRCASE GRID WALL STRUCTURE CLADDING TYPICAL CURTAIN WALL SKY SIGN EXTERNAL MAINTENANCE FIRE PROTECTION FIRE SHUTTER IAC WALL

INTERNAL BLIND

SIGN

EQUIPMENT BOXES

REFUSE DISPOSAL

FIRE WALL

LIGHTING

LIGHTING

CEILING SYSTEM

DOCUMENT HANDLING

INNER SUNSCOOP

CONTROL DOOR

ESCALATOR

LORRY HOIST

SUBFLOOR SERVICES
INSULATION

TROX BOX

ELECTRICAL BOX

BEAM CLADDING

STEEL STRUCTURE

HMT
Ako
JAPAN (12)

Tachikawa
Tokyo
JAPAN (3)

Kawada
Tokyo
JAPAN (3)

Erco
Lüdenscheid
WEST GERMANY (21)

Erco
Lüdenscheid
WEST GERMANY (21)

Centralsug
SWEDEN (29)

Getz
California
USA (27)

Siemens
Traunreut
WEST GERMANY (20)

Erco
Lüdenscheid
WEST GERMANY (21)

Naka/Citoh
Tokyo
JAPAN (3)

GIG/LISTO
Linz
AUSTRIA (2)

Tajima
Tokyo
JAPAN (3)

Otis
Stadthagen
WEST GERMANY (13)

Schindler
Switzerland (33)

NEW ZEALAND (8)

Trox
UK (4)

Ackermann
UK (4)

GIG/LISTO
Linz
AUSTRIA (2)

British Steel
Middlesbrough
UK (5)

Cupples
St Louis
USA (5)

Cupples
St Louis
USA (5)

Cupples
St Louis
USA (5)

GIG/LISTO
Linz
AUSTRIA (2)

Stephens & Carter
Kent
UK (22)

Morceau
London
UK (4)

Bolton Brady
West Yorkshire
UK (11)

IAC
New York
USA (25)

Pagula
Frankfurt
WEST GERMANY (24)

Naka/Citoh
Sapporo
JAPAN (28)

Acconci
FINLAND (19)

TRICOSAL GmbH & Cokg
Jilsertiassen
WEST GERMANY (9)

FOAMGLASS
Pittsburgh
USA (37)

GIG/LISTO
Linz
AUSTRIA (2)

MBM
Mockmühl
WEST GERMANY (7)

Naka/Citoh
Tokyo
JAPAN (3)

Elemeta
London
UK (4)

MBM
Mockmühl
WEST GERMANY (7)

Otis
Liverpool
UK (14)

NLM
Tokyo
JAPAN (3)

Trox
Düsseldorf
WEST GERMANY (6)

Ackermann
Gummersbach
WEST GERMANY (10)

Johnson Control
Milwaukee
USA (15)

Trox
Thetford
UK (22)

Philips
Eindhoven
WEST GERMANY (18)

KAWADA
Tokyo
JAPAN (3)

Freudenberg
Weinheim
WEST GERMANY (31)

KITCHEN CEILING

FACE PANEL

STONE FLOOR FINISH

WATERPROOFING

WATERPROOFING

KITCHENETTE

LINER AT
BOARD ROOM

DEMOUNTABLE
PARTITION

GLAZED FIREWALL

EXTERNAL SUNSCOOP

LIFT

LIFT SHAFT GLAZING

A/C OUTLET

ELECTRICAL
FLOOR OUTLET

BMS

LINEAR GRILLE

P A SYSTEM

BRIDGE

Ahrend
HOLLAND (23)

Herman Miller
Michigan
USA (36)

Simon
Pesaro
ITALY (34)

Sunar Hauserman
Edmonton
CANADA (35)

Technomarm
Turin
ITALY (32)

GIG/LISTO
Linz
AUSTRIA (2)

H.H Robertson
Indiann
USA (26)

Thorn EMI
London
UK (4)

Thorn EMI
London
UK (4)

Interface
Georgia
USA (30)

FURNITURE FURNITURE FURNITURE FURNITURE STONE FLOOR FINISH UNDERBELLY FLOOR SUPPORT SMOKE DETECTOR HALON CARPET RUBBER

123

32.4.
Fixing arrangement of cladding panels. 1 Unistrut fixed to structural member through fire blanket; 2 cast cleat; 3 extruded aluminium edge section; 4 weather seals

32.5.
Largest panel being positioned over joint between truss and hanger

glass. Blinds were omitted from the north-facing windows with their splendid views. A *brise soleil* was applied to each of the Bank's facades and it also acts as a walkway for cleaning and maintenance of the facade. At each end of the walkway there are glazed panels that open to form access doors from the interior. These also serve to allow the mandatory 2% of floor area smoke vents (Figure 32.6).

The framing to the curtain walling consists of extruded aluminium vertical mullions with a c.h.s. outer flange and perforated web. These are connected by aluminium castings consisting of an upper and lower spigot which slide into the outer tubes of the mullion. This does most of the structural work, providing a connection capable of accepting vertical movement of +20 to −60 mm. This cast connector is in turn fixed back to the horizontal support rails to the floor slabs by means of T-bracket connectors offering both vertical and horizontal adjustment (Figure 32.7). This casting forms a key to the whole assembly, as it not only supports the ends of the mullions back to the structure, allowing for a large degree of movement, but also provides a connection point for the cast aluminium brackets which support the *brise soleil* and maintenance catwalks. The aluminium brackets were manufactured by a vacuum-evacuated die, and over 4000 brackets were required for the whole building (Figure 32.8). According to Davies:

> This humble component is as finely engineered a piece of metalwork as you'll find in any aerospace factory. The brackets are perforated with round holes that recall Foster's elegant metal furniture designs and the louvres are set at an angle precisely calculated to reduce glare from below, but allow a view down from above. They form a prominent feature of the facade and perhaps for this reason they have been installed over the whole of the north elevation facing the harbour, even though this side of the building rarely receives direct sunlight.

Structural silicone glazing has been used to fix the glass back to the framing members and to form the horizontal joints between glazing. As with the joints between panels, this silicone glazing is visible at ground-floor levels. The glazing system also allows drainage from the fascia at each floor level (Figure 32.9).

The Bank exemplifies the quality of and attention to detailing that is necessary to produce a building of this quality. It is here where the constructional detail becomes an essential feature of design, where at all levels total commitment by the architects towards the buildability of their design ideas would be required. Students of architecture should not underestimate the degree of time

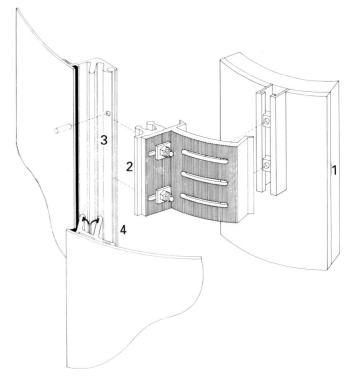

32.4.

32.5.

32.6.
External walkways

32.8.
Exploded isometric of bracket assembly. 1. Cast aluminium walkway support bracket; 2 extruded aluminium fins; 3 aluminium fascia; 4 horizontal glazing frame; 5 extruded aluminium mullion; 6 perimeter steel r.h.s. fixed back to slab; 7 steel bracket; 8 adjustable T-section; 9 cast aluminium bracket with steel spigots to fit cladding mullions

32.7.
Mock-up of bracket

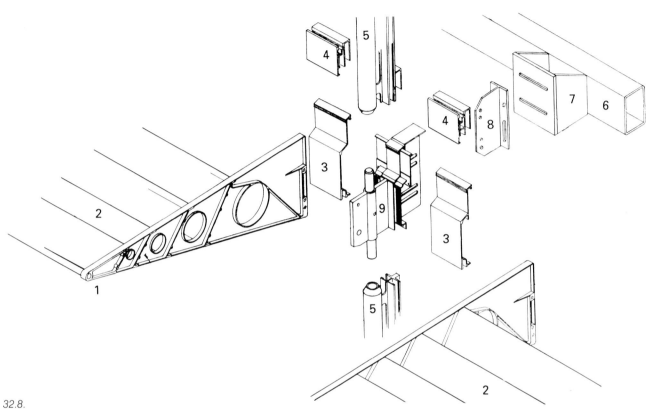

32.8.

32.7.

32.6.

32.9.
*Section of glazing cill showing
drainage from fascia at each floor*

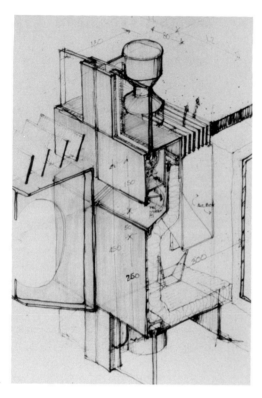

32.9.

and energy this level of commitment would require. It is also interesting to see the ways where elements of one system are re-used in different locations to provide a continuity in the design. For example, mullions from the curtain walling were adapted to form parts of the space frame trusses that support the glazing to the lift lobbies and entrance canopies. In this way, the vocabulary of detailing becomes the language of the design.

References

This building has been widely published throughout the world and we have only here briefly touched on one aspect of the design. For further information the following sources are also useful.

Anon., 'Two engineered solutions', *Architects' Journal*, 22 October 1986, pp. 79–94. This shows a comparison between the construction of the Lloyds Building in London (see Case Study 14) and the Bank, and includes some useful information on the design and development of the structure, cladding and services.

Chaslin, F., *Norman Foster*, Elector Monitor, 1986, pp. 126–154. This summary of the construction includes some excellent early sketches showing the fixing of the cladding to the structure using Unistrut type anchors and the silicone butt jointing in the glazing. There is also an excellent sketch showing the fascia member between the curtain walling and the junction to the floor edge beams. (Similar information is contained in a study of the building in *Architecture d'Ajourd'hui*.)

Davies, C., 'Building the Bank', *Architectural Review*, April 1986, pp. 82–106. In this entire issue dedicated to the Bank, Davies' description of the detail developments is a useful contribution towards understanding the technical nature of the building, with exploded isometrics showing the interfaces between the various components.

Lambot, I., *The New Headquarters for the Hongkong and Shanghai Banking Corporation*, Ian Lambot, Hong Kong, 1985. This is an excellent survey of photographs showing the sequence of assembly of the building from groundworks in 1983 to the official opening on 7 April 1986. As such, it represents the most invaluable and unique guide to students wishing to learn more about the construction not only of this building but also of any building using component technology. Most useful from the point of view of this case study are photographs 72 and 73, showing the location of the steel frame and the fixing of the wall cladding (photographs 62 and 91). There is also an excellent series of photographs on the construction of the suspended flooring with service ducts below. An amusing contrast is shown in the centre page between the hand-tied bamboo scaffolding extensively used throughout the construction and the sophistication of the building elements around it.

Seddon, C., 'Norman Foster's Hong Kong and Shanghai Bank', *Architect (Australia)*, October 1986. This contains a summary of the design construction process, including a description of the sources of building materials and elements used in the Bank, and of the tolerances required for the structure and main components. For example, 'The maximum wind load generating a 4 second oscillation at the top of the building of 300 mm resolves out at 7 mm lateral movement per floor'.

Winter, J., 'Comparing products', *Architects' Journal*, 22 October 1986, pp. 97–102. This article also compares products used at Lloyds and the Bank and gives information on the manufacturers involved.

New Studios and Galleries, Liverpool
Architects
Dave King and Rod McAllister

General

Designed by Dave King and Rod McAllister in association with the Gerald Beech Partnership, the new studio and galleries in Liverpool provide 1500 m² of teaching and exhibition space as the major part of the refurbishment of the School of Architecture to accommodate the recent merger with the University's Department of Building Engineering (Figure 33.1).

Structure

The new design spans across the roof of the existing extension to the School of Architecture, an early 1930s Modernist building by Reilly, Budden and Marshal. The lightweight structure, which uses a central arcade of tubular columns, consists of steel beams and purlins supporting a metal-decked roof system over the three-tier open-plan studio and exhibition space. The beams are tapered at their ends and pin jointed to flanged capitals at the column heads (Figure 33.2). Loads are carried down to the foundations mainly through the concrete core and the structure is designed to transmit minimal weight to the existing steel-framed building. Purlins are spaced at 1575 and 2400 mm centres and are carried through to the outer walls, where they continue in the vertical plane to act as cladding posts (Figure 33.3). Junctions between structural members are straightforward and bold in recognition of the fact that they will be exposed internally as well as externally (Figures 33.4–33.6).

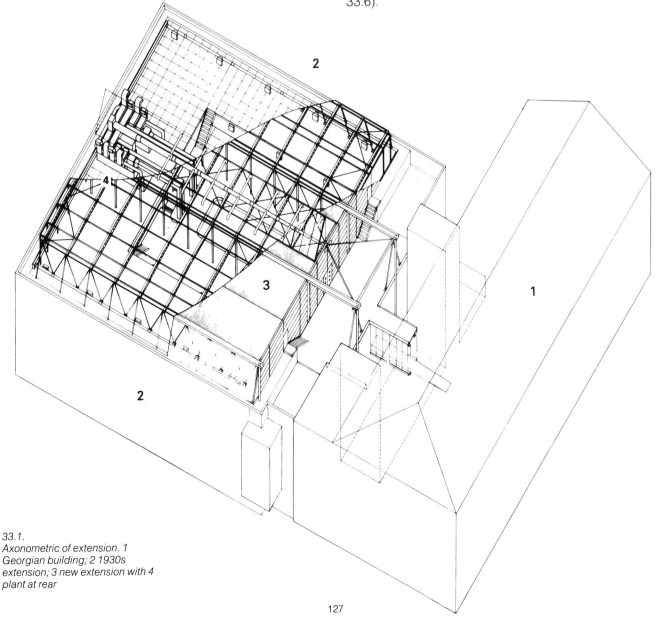

33.1.
Axonometric of extension. 1 Georgian building; 2 1930s extension; 3 new extension with 4 plant at rear

33.2.
Model of central arcade showing
tapered beams pinned to
columns

33.3.
Computer model of central
arcade showing different levels

33.2.

33.3.

33.4.
*Steelwork detail showing bracing
to tapered beams*

33.5.
*Steelwork detail showing bracing
of lower flange of beam to
counteract wind uplift on flat roof*

33.6.
Gable wall

The structural engineers for the extension were the local practice of Roy Billington Associates and the steelwork was prefabricated by Roydens of St Helens.

Cladding

The cladding itself is a lightweight 70 mm thick foam sandwich employing microprofile steel sheeting on both inner and outer faces. It is of similar type to that used on Foster Associates' Renault Building at Swindon, being manufactured to fine tolerances and employing a matt silver PVF^2 finish. Jointing is 22 mm butyl rubber gasket in the vertical plane and 8 mm polysulphide pointing horizontally (Figure 33.7).

Unusually for such a building, the cladding system is only on the gable faces, the two sides being glazed (Figures 33.7 and 33.9). It is confined to specifically delineated panels between structural members, and doors, where they occur, do not pierce the cladding itself. The concept is to use cladding as 'lightweight stone' with a strong joint pattern, rather than to 'skin' the building, as is more often the case.

Glazing is a combination of raked patent-glazed outer walls and a central full-length roof light. Although ordinary 6 mm toughened glass was appropriate at the lower level, solar gain necessitated the use of 16 mm three-skin Makrolon on the rooflight. The material, imported from West Germany, gives the appearance of reeded glass and is surprisingly transparent. The effect of bright sun is to reflect a long line of light the full length of the glazing and, therefore, seemingly intensify the light source.

Services

The building's systems are completely integrated with the structure. Electrical installation is concealed within structural members and special light fittings employing a combination of tungsten-halogen fluorescent and discharge lamps give an overall clean white effect.

Mechanical services are exposed, as are internal gutters and rainwater pipes. Another unusual innovation is that the central extract plant room is placed, for demonstration purposes, within the studio space. A specially designed tamperproof control panel constantly monitors the plant operation and gives all relevant zone information at a glance. The services were designed by Henry Gun & Why and Dave Dutton of Liverpool University.

Millfield Library
College of Technology
BELFAST

33.4.

33.5.

33.6.

33.7.
Gutter and downpipe detail

33.8.
Cladding fixing detail. 1 22 mm
butyl rubber gasket; 2 0.6 mm
steel outer skin; 3 0.6 mm steel
inner skin; 4 70 mm expanded
polystyrene; 5 low-density foam
seal; 6 self-tapping screw; 7 3 mm
galvanized steel fixing plate; 8
packer; 9 120 × 60 mm r.h.s.

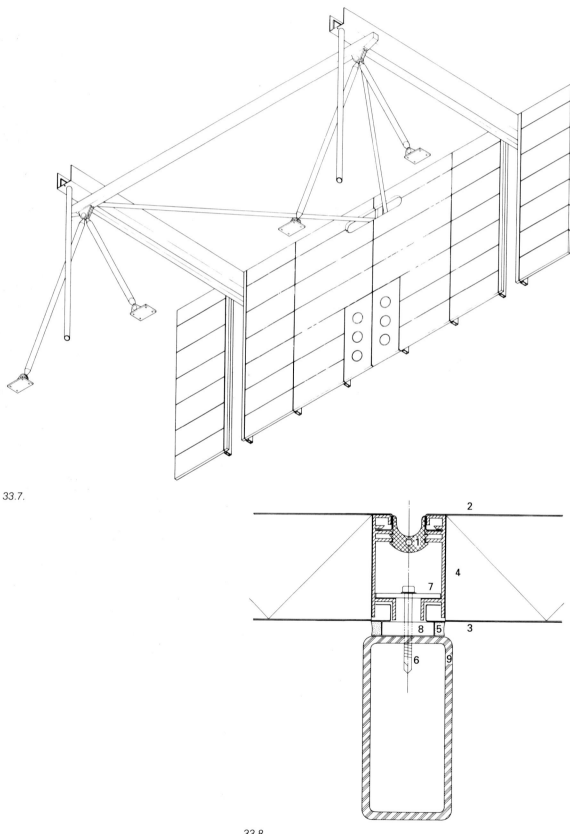

33.7.

33.8.

33.9.
Corner detail. 1 Cladding panels;
2 6 mm toughened glass in raked
patent glazing system; 3 gutter
and downpipe; 4 existing roof of
1930s extension

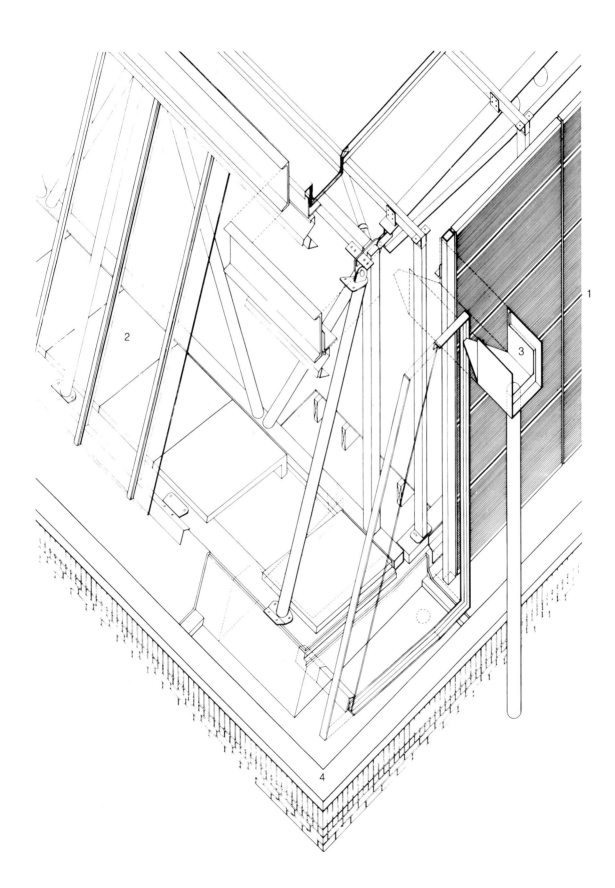

1

2

3

4

Finishes

Finishes are simple and direct. Stainless and galvanized steel are left untreated and the structure is painted throughout with a silicon alkyd aluminium paint which has the property of retaining its sheen. Conventional silver paints tend to chalk quickly. The floor finish throughout is green 'artificial grass', which is carried through to a south-facing terrace.

Conclusion

The design's objective is to present a combination of classical order and technological expression with an exciting special concept … its precise silver cladding, stainless steel rainwater system and sharp triangular rooflight draw more inspiration from recent developments in Switzerland and Italy than from current British Post-modernism. It is intended that the extensive use of exposed services and the direct constructional language will encourage its use as a unique teaching environment.

The project uses a deliberately strong aesthetic to maintain its presence in the context of the school's existing buildings. Its sense of balance and logical juxtaposition of elements are combined with an accurate contemporary style to enhance its rare status as purpose-made 'School Design'.

References

Anon., 'Dave King and Rod McAllister, architects', *Architectural Review*, May 1989, pp. 40–41.

Index of Names

MiL
N18s
12842
£37.50